Chasing Carrots

won't help you find your purpose if you were born to love bananas.

A Life-Changing Adventure
By Jimi Gibson

Charleston, SC

Published by Jimi Gibson Creative, LLC
Charleston, SC 29407

Copy editing by Joyce Gibson. Additional story feedback by Dana Gibson, David Gibson, Harold Gibson, Ken Gibson, Pierce Marrs, Brenda Sanders, and Art Trotter. Character design by Jimi Gibson. Illustrations by Wyatt Miles and Anighosh.

ISBN: 978-1-7360526-0-0 Hardback
ISBN: 978-1-7360526-1-7 Kindle

Printed in the United States of America

To my family

"There are two great days in a person's life–
the day we are born and the day we discover why."
– William Barclay

Seagull Arrives

Chapter One – Seagull Introduces Monkey

In a few days Monkey will be tricked into making a deal that could change the course of his life forever. It's a deal with the devil, actually with seven of his minions, seven sisters you will meet very soon.

Sorry, I should have introduced myself. I'm Seagull. I'm on my way to help a little fella who has lost his way in life. Things haven't turned out the way he expected. It's my job to show Monkey how off-track things have really gotten.

Distractions are the culprit. Monkey has been chasing carrots. Carrots have stolen years, ruined friendships, and made him a stranger to who he was born to be.

Birthdays are the best times for me to do my work, times to check in. Lost souls often reflect, "Am I where I thought I would be in my life by now? What happened to that dream I once had?" I'm about to visit someone just like that. Monkey's birthday is getting close. He's no ordinary monkey. In fact, he is quite talented. He's just gotten so distracted he's forgotten who he really is.

You see, I rarely find those who consider their birthdays gifts. I'm talking about the actual day they were born. They don't consider a talent or skill part of the birthday present they are given. Don't you see? The day of your birth is your first opportunity to step into a world waiting for your uniqueness. What a glorious realization if you'll let yourself drink it in!

I probably should tell you a few more details. Monkey lives at the Carnival. I'm soon to be the only visitor to the Carnival whose sole pursuit is *not* chasing carrots.

You see, the Carnival is a place of illusion, a full departure from wisdom. It's a selfish place of foolish pursuits. Carrots of every kind intoxicate the mind and lure you closer to the edge of forgetting who you really are.

Monkey is close to that edge. Monkey has convinced himself he is a rabbit and stars in a magic show at a grand theater inside the Carnival. Keep this in mind. Things aren't always as they appear in the Carnival. Reality is distorted for those who have given in to the pursuit of carrots. You don't think straight. You're about as far away from truth and wisdom as you can be.

Excuse me for just a minute. This landing is tricky. I've just cleared the tree line and I'll be arriving at the Carnival in a few seconds. The fog is thick, and I really don't want to smash into the side of that Ferris Wheel again.

Well, I've said enough already. It's not my story to tell. I'll let "Rabbit" (Monkey) tell you about his adventure.

The Magic Show

Chapter Two – A Rabbit in the Hat?

This is it, my favorite part of the show. I waited for a glimpse at the audience from my secret hiding place. Magician is right on cue. And three, four, "Ladies and Gentlemen, the most famous illusion in all of magic: An empty silk hat, containing nothing but the hopes and dreams of a humble magician." He walked towards the front of the stage. "You have been an engaging and appreciative crowd. My finale this evening is but a moment away. The simple wave of my hand will transform…," said Magician.

He always dragged that part out a few seconds too long. If I ran this show, I would speed up this cue. Timing is a strange thing to get right. The personality of an illusion has an ebb and flow. Too soon and you haven't built up the right amount of tension. Too long and the audience wonders why you're dragging it out. The telltale sign is a yawn or a brief glance at a watch. The spell is broken. These people have paid to escape their lives and experience some magic. Make them anxious to get back to the real world and you haven't done your job. "And now, ladies and gentlemen, the rabbit from the hat!"

It happened all at once! He announced my arrival, and I get yanked from the dark into the warm glow of the stage light. I savored every minute that I dangled from Magician's hand, gently swaying in the brilliance of the spotlights that washed the stage. The glow was a sunshine that felt like the beach on a perfect summer day. From my vantage point I saw the shadowy shapes of the crowd pointing and waving. I concentrated to avoid waving back. That would break character, a big taboo as the assistant. I've got to be the rabbit they've come to see. Hold for 1, 2, and blackout. The stage was dark. The audience was on their feet. Standing ovation!

The blackout was the most dramatic ending you could get. It said to the audience, "That's it, show over." I've done his show 372 times to be exact, and the blackout is what I waited for every time. There's an afterimage that remains for a second or two when the lights go out. Amateur performers move to their next cue at the moment of blackout, but sitting in the audience, the visible motion looks bad. The half-lit image of a performer not waiting for the afterimage to fade said "Amateur" with a capital A. Other performers don't get it. I guess that's what separates those who want to master their craft from those who never will—the details. Mediocrity is defined by the sheer ugliness of a rushed blackout.

Every show was a ride on the coaster. Magician and the sisters took their bows. One of the sisters, Pride, gave me a wink. The curtain closed, and I couldn't wait for the next show.

The press would be here for a reception after the show, so the backstage area had to be spotless. Magician had interviews lined up, and we had to be ready for photos.

Five of the sisters covered the illusions and prepared the backstage for the wandering eyes of over-curious reporters. It was my job to lock the prop cabinet and bring Magician his coffee. Another sister, Laziness, always headed back to her dressing room for a quick nap right after the show, and Pride escorted Magician to the lobby for his first interview. The caterers had been setting up all day. I was sure the refreshments would be incredible. Magician spared no expense in putting on a different kind of show for the media.

Magician was eccentric. I guess that's what made him so attractive. When he isn't on stage, he claims he can't see a thing. Dark glasses concealed closed eyes. One of the sisters escorts him everywhere. He calls the girls his windows to the world. On stage, he sees everything. Bathed in the spotlight, Magician feeds himself with applause.

I grabbed his cup of coffee, added three teaspoons of salt (eccentric), and headed down the service hallway of the theater to the lobby. Unused illusion cases lined the dimly lit corridor. Each box contained a custom-built prop costing thousands of dollars. Magician was good, really good, and we had played to sold-out shows for years. How would I ever be able to afford big illusions? I had big dreams, but the pressure to get there squeezed my chest like when I held hands with sisters Greed and Envy during the final bow. The coffee smelled bitter, but Magician claimed it was the sweetest nectar next to carrot juice.

I heard the muffled sound of conversation from down the hall. Voices got louder as I rounded the corner. I listened for a break in Magician's speech and turned the knob. I eased the door open about an inch to look before barging in. I wasn't going to be the one who ruined an interview or spoiled a photo. Magician answered questions seated behind a red velvet-covered table located under the show poster. Everyone else was seated beneath the grand chandelier in the middle of the atrium. The scene was more formal than usual.

A young reporter in the front row stood up, "You have had five years of consecutive sold-out shows in this town. Where does all the money go?"

As I headed for the side of Magician's table, I wondered how Magician would answer. I was curious too. The seven sisters were all standing behind Magician, still in their closing number outfits. They were the most expensive and most revealing of the twelve costume changes in the show. Pride had her hand on Magician's left shoulder as he responded. "We're so humbled to have set a record here at the Grand Illusion Theater for the most consecutive sold out performances. To show our gratitude to the community, I've decided that all of the ticket sales will be donated to the favorite charities of my seven assistants." Spontaneous applause erupted and cameras flashed while pens danced on paper notebooks.

Another question from the crowd came from an older, hunched-over man in the back row, "I hear that your rival, the Man of Miracles, will be opening at the Paradise Theater next week. Are you ready for the competition?"

I had just made it behind the table as the gentleman finished his question, disguised as a jab. I knew Magician liked his coffee immediately after the show, so I reached up to place it beside his left hand. Pride had stepped back to let me by. Wrath and Envy both leaned in to comfort Magician with a gentle hand on his back. Before I could get the mug high enough, Magician felt for my ears, lowered his arm and knocked the coffee from my hand. I let go of the handle; hot liquid burned my leg as I fell against Wrath's right boot. The metal spikes on the front of her boot jabbed my back.

The media was unaware of my pain but immediately reacted to the disturbance. Pride leaned down to pick me up, careful not to stain her dress with coffee and unsure whether the spike had drawn blood. It hadn't.

Magician placed the empty mug on the table and wiped the warm coffee off his hand with the table drape. "A clumsy Rabbit is still worth keeping on the show, and we certainly can't cry over spilled coffee, can we? Maybe he wants his own show. This rabbit has a talent for stealing the spotlight." Laughter from the crowd was another metaphorical spike in the back. Was Magician's stunt simply to avoid answering the reporter's question?

The hunched-over man stood up and repeated his question, "Are you worried?"

Envy stepped back and Wrath helped Magician up. He didn't say a word. The room went dark. The spotlight, focused on the show poster, moved down to frame Magician's face. He adjusted his dark glasses. Pride had put me down. I crawled to the side and managed to hop onto the green sofa against the wall to avoid being part of another accident.

Magician spoke, "My magic is untouchable. The moon is disgraced that it must compete with my rising tide of fans. The sun is ashamed when compared to the splendor of my production. I alone am responsible for my talent, my wisdom and my riches." The spotlight grew to a full body spread. Magician climbed onto the table as all the sisters wrapped themselves around his legs. Magician raised his voice, "You ask about competition? I have prepared a banquet for all of you. There are no boundaries to the sumptuous pleasures that await." Magician pointed and looked directly at the man who posed the question. "After seeing my show and drinking my wine, you will know that this mere Man of Miracles cannot compete. If you see his show, I guarantee you will darken the doorstep of this theatre again and request an audience with the King of Magic. Now, follow me."

For a full five-seconds Magician and the seven sisters remained completely motionless. Magician knew his craft. They waited, then it came. Every reporter climbed into the palm of his hand. The standing ovation lasted for three and a half minutes. "Long live the king," they chanted. Sisters Lust and Gluttony lead the group into the adjoining room. Still sitting on the sofa as the crowd moved into the banquet room, I soaked in what had just happened. Magician was a genius and I had just witnessed the coronation of a King.

It felt good to be on something soft. I ran my arm in between the sofa cushions in hopes that I would come back with a handful of coins. This was the perfect spot for the theater crowd to let a pocket cough up loose change before the house opened. What's this? My fingers grazed across a stiff piece of paper lodged in the springs. Another playing card lost from the free trick in the popcorn box, I was sure. "Three of spades," I guessed out loud. I pulled my hand out from under the cushion. It wasn't a playing card at all. It was a hand-written note that read, "Happy Birthday. Quit the show. You were born for something much bigger. You should follow the Man of Miracles." I put it in the outer pocket of my shoulder bag and joined the party in the banquet room.

Chapter Three – A Second Invitation

Magician delivered on his promise. The display in the banquet room was legendary: fountains of carrot juice in orange, purple, red, white, and yellow. Carrots were chopped, sautéed, fried, steamed, and cooked in soups and stews. Carrot cakes and carrot puddings were garnished with the carrot greens that numbed the tongue like sushi from the poisonous puffer fish. The sisters scented the room with a perfume that loosened conversation and washed away inhibitions.

Carrots give hills to the flatness of life, like the wooden roller coaster. The anticipation of the climb is the foreplay of the carrot chase. The rush down is the full submission to their power.

After the reporters had gorged themselves on the cornucopia of carrot delights, they stumbled into the street at just about midnight. I started cleaning the banquet room. Sack after sack of empty bottles made the side hallway of the backstage seem twice as long. Every trip to the vacant lot to dispose of the bottles behind the theater got slower and slower. I was so tired and just wanted to go to bed.

The air outside felt perfect. The only light came

from the moon's glow. It replaced a burned-out flood-light on the side of the building. I set up three bottles and picked up a stone from the driveway and tossed it.

"You missed," said a voice from my left.

"You could do better?" I asked.

Seagull landed on the ground beside the bottles and smacked them with his wing.

"Done," he said.

"You cheated," I headed back inside for what I hoped would be my last trip.

"Wait. How was the party?" Seagull asked.

Seagull had been around for a few days and always wanted to talk when I took out the trash. I gave him a polite, but quick answer and hoped he would fly away. "Epic," I said.

Seagull wouldn't give up, "The early edition of the paper is already out, and I can see that the headlines will be great for business."

Seagull took off his newspaper hat, opened it and read in a voice too loud for the late hour, "King of Magic rules over the Grand Illusion Theatre. A new finale will be announced soon."

The wind picked up, and Seagull struggled to get the paper folded and back on his head. The stench of all the garbage hit my face. Magician's parties had become more frequent in the last few weeks, and the rotten scraps and fermented carrot juice stung my nose. Clouds covered the moon and my light vanished.

"It looks like rain," I said in a feeble attempt to head off a long discussion.

"It won't rain," Seagull said. "Magician boasts of a

gift he does not give, just like those clouds that refuse to rain."

Seagull always talked in riddles I couldn't understand. I tried to be considerate, "I'll be right back." I hurried to the front of the theater to look for bottles stashed behind plants or carrot cake stuck to the floor. Magician boasts of a gift he does not give? A new finale? I was the finale. Seagull made no sense. Did Seagull's comment refer to the note in the couch? If I quit the show a new finale was needed? I'm not quitting the show.

Finally, the long day was over. I finished emptying the last bag of bottles and bolted the stage door. My hat was stage left. I mentally planned how I would approach my hat. I'd hop once, turn around, and collapse into the opening. I loved appearing from my hat in the show and curling up inside it at night. What else could a rabbit need?

As I approached my hat, I noticed something leaned against the brim. I'd have to delay my backwards flop.

"Oh," I blurted out uncontrollably and heard my voice echo off the back wall. There was an envelope artfully placed against the brim of my hat. It was layered with gold scroll work, engraved type and was addressed, "Mr. Rabbit." Another note? I pulled the card out, careful not to crumple the flap. "You are invited to a birthday party." I read the front of the card, not realizing that my voice had gotten louder. "The sisters will meet you at the Ferris Wheel at nine o'clock in the morning." A birthday party at the carnival? I read on, "Be prepared to make a wish."

I hadn't noticed the small type under the shadow of my hand. "We'll provide the birthday cake and candle. Meet us in YOUR birthday car." I placed the card back in the envelope, leaned it against my hat and hopped in without touching the rim.

I drifted off to sleep dreaming of the wish I would make, the cake I would eat, and the riddle I needed to solve before riding the Ferris wheel. Was the note in the sofa cushions for me? Why would someone think I'd even consider leaving this show? Who was it from?

Birthday Party

Chapter Four – Carrots at the Carnival

"Happy Birthday!" I greeted myself and crawled out of my hat. The show was closed today, so I'd have the entire day to myself. How long would the party last? Had the sisters bought me a present?

"Find YOUR birthday car," I read again. I grabbed a book of matches. If the sisters forget matches, I wouldn't be able to make a wish. I checked the clock above the stage door and left in plenty of time to get to the giant wheel. I bolted the lock in slow motion to avoid drawing the attention of Seagull if he were nearby. "YOUR birthday car," was a puzzle that sounded like Seagull talk. Maybe I should ask him for help.

The anticipation of the day ahead made the walk easier. I couldn't allow thoughts of quitting the show ruin *my* day. The theater was inside the carnival, but I had a little walk to get to the main area. As I crossed the edge of the carrot patch, I saw the big tents with their triangle-shaped flags poking into the fog above.

I tripped on a row of carrots, not paying attention to my crooked path. Every day customers ate tons of carrot treats. It made sense to plop the carnival in the middle of the supply. The Ferris wheel, "earl of isdo," was my lighthouse. The riddle? I had to solve it before I reached the wheel. I felt like a new rabbit. Birthdays were always a chance to start fresh.

I'm sure the sisters had arranged for the party to start so early because the carnival didn't open until ten. I had never had the carnival to myself for an entire hour. I rounded the edge of the ticket booth. A padlock secured the back door, Frog wasn't there yet. You couldn't really enter the main flow of the Carnival without passing the ticket booth.

The eerie quietness of the morning was interrupted by a worker crossing the path in front of me. All the ride operators, midway staff, and food sellers were pigs and wore special shirts so you could find them at any booth. A few pigs moved in the shadows, unpacking boxes, turning on lights, and hanging new prizes.

Something about the blackness of the morning didn't feel right. The choreography of neon and laughter was absent.

As I approached the main area of the midway, I stopped and looked. There stood the giant wheel. I had been focused on getting to the wheel and forgot to admire the tallest ride at the Carnival. The midway is the most exciting part of any carnival. It's the hub of all the action—games, rides, and food of all varieties.

The Ferris wheel was covered in a blanket of fog. I waved my hands to clear the fog and leaned in and looked for clues. I had to solve the riddle of *my* birthday car. The fog blocked my view of any numbers on the side of the Ferris wheel cars.

"Hi, Rabbit," they said in unison. I was expecting all seven sisters. I could see only three, Gluttony, Greed and Pride.

Gluttony put me on her shoulder, and we ran towards a food trailer with a very large bright orange carrot on top.

"Two large carrots," she said as she leaned towards the window trying to catch a glimpse of the carrots inside the trailer. "They dip them in chocolate here." She directed that last part to me, assuring me we had picked the right seller. Pig was still setting up but turned to fill our order.

I took a bite, felt the blood rush from my head and a dizzy sickness come over me. A sour taste burned the back of my throat, lightheaded. I couldn't afford to pass out. My mind raced in wobbly circles.

"Another?" Gluttony shoved the remaining carrot in my mouth. Why not, no need to take it slow. Gluttony had a way of convincing me. Her warm smile and gentle voice melted my ability to consider any other choice.

"Enough eating, come with me," Greed grabbed my hand. The tight feeling in my stomach shifted to my chest. Gluttony stayed behind, holding what was left of my carrots. Greed was intense, focused, and headed for neon and noise. The workers had started to awaken the carnival. Our theatre was just inside the main gate. It was still early in the morning, but the carnival was always dark. A thick blanket of fog hung overhead and blocked light from reaching any part of the carnival. The darkness helped the magic. I readjusted my hand in her tight grip. Blinking lights from everywhere danced off her silver bracelets and gold rings, most of them given to her by Magician. My chest clinched tighter.

We approached the midway, and I knew we were headed for the milk bottles. It's not a game of skill; it's a cheat. The bottles were weighted.

"How much did you bring?" She asked. Greed reached in my satchel and grabbed a couple of coins from the stash at the bottom. This place was paradise. I had money and I was ready to play.

Two coins got you three balls. The rules of the cheat were simple. Six fake milk bottles were stacked pyramid-style on an eight-inch round table. I wouldn't win unless the table was empty. It looked easy. That's the bait.

The worker behind the counter set the balls on the short wall between us. Greed paid Pig at the counter. "Get all the bottles on the first throw, pick a prize from the top shelf. Two balls? Middle shelf. Three balls? Bottom shelf. No leaning," Pig said automatically, like it was the billionth time.

Because rabbits are short, my angle was different. "POW, I got all six." The bottles tumbled off and made a hollow sound as they hit the base of the table. Their upright position on the ground was another clue that each was hiding a cement plug.

"Lucky throw," Pig said. "What'll it be?" He stared blankly not even looking in my direction.

"Golden carrot, top shelf," I said.

I dropped two more coins in the box. Smart bosses never let the crew handle money. The pigs only made change, handed out balls, and gave away prizes. Greed stood behind me with her hands on my shoulders.

My chest grew tighter. I felt her dig her fingers in as the bottles made their sound again.

"Play again," she said as she stroked the back of my neck. The sound of the coins dropping and bottles falling faded into the background, and I focused on the hundred carrot prizes rammed between the narrow shelves above me. I wanted them all. It didn't matter if it was a carrot I could eat or collect. I was hooked on them.

"More. Play again," Greed said. Greed's direct commands were different from the comfort of Gluttony's purr.

I looked down. Pig just stood there, holding three balls, not making eye contact with me or Greed. Dirty water dripped onto his left sleeve from a rusty bracket above. He didn't care that I was winning. Pig looked hungry.

I reached down into my satchel with the intent of repeating the rhythm but handed him my two coins. "Here, take the money, buy some food," I said. Pig's gaze shifted for the first time as he reached to take the money.

"Rabbit, you fool," Greed said. "Never give it away." Her hand closed around mine before Pig could grab them. As her nails dug into my wrist, Pig's eyes turned glassy. My mouth went dry.

"How's my little guy doing?" asked Gluttony. She was back with carrot juice. I took the bottle from her with my left hand. I dropped the coins back into my satchel. Greed watched.

The tiny lumps of carrot tumbled down my throat. The chill of the juice raised my fur at the base of my spine. It had always done that since I was young. The strap on my satchel dug into my left shoulder from the weight of my winnings. My eyes wouldn't focus and my right arm ached. Gluttony held me from the right side and Greed took my left. The carrots had stolen my balance.

"Now he's mine," said Pride who had been flirting with some workers who recognized her from our show. "I love signing autographs." The four of us made a crooked path away from the midway and towards the Ferris wheel and the rides.

Carnivals are judged by the size of the wheel. Double ones went for height. Single ones boasted diameter and colored lights. This one was single and touched the clouds. The name, "earl of isdo," glowed through the fog. Something didn't look right.

"Is the Ferris wheel going in the wrong direction?" I asked Pride.

"It's always been that way. Don't the amber lights make me look like a movie star?" she asked.

The House of Mirth was beside the giant wheel's ticket turnstile. Pride headed for the laughing-face archway that marked the entrance. A young pig tripped on the metal step ahead of us. I stopped too quickly to avoid landing on top of her, and the liquid shifted in my stomach. I didn't feel well. The fun house didn't sound like a good choice for me right now.

"I can't wait. It's my favorite of favorites," Pride said. "We'll get through the mirror maze faster than anyone." Was she serious? Pride checked her make-up, fixed her hair, and adjusted her sequined dress in front of every reflective surface in sight. We'll be in there the rest of the day. Pride handed me the tickets.

Gluttony and Greed decided to stay outside while Pride convinced me I was Rabbit enough to handle the spinning tunnel at the end. Pride always made you feel better about yourself; like you could do anything.

We were almost to the entrance. Holding Pride's hand made the pain in my stomach go away. She leaned over and whispered, "These people that work here are so pathetic. If they knew we were part of the show, they'd let us in for free." It was our turn. A younger pig staring into nothingness tore our tickets and pointed to the first door. As he handed the stubs back, Pride stopped, looked over her shoulder and asked, loud enough for everyone on the platform to hear, "We're in the big magic show at the Grand Illusion Theatre; Don't you recognize us?" The younger pig didn't answer.

I was right. We made good time through the first part of the fun house, over shaking floors and around moving walls. When we entered the hall of mirrors, we paused at the first panel. Pride put on more lipstick, licked her teeth and fixed a twisted earring. We finally moved after she pushed her hair behind her ears. Pride was ahead of me; she turned left and banged her forehead into a panel of glass.

"Ouch, please don't bruise, please." She wasn't hurt, just surprised. The floor was painted with a path of carrots, but the challenge was to figure out which carrots guided your path forward, which were behind a glass divider, and which were reflections in a mirrored panel. Reflections and see-through panels trick the eye.

Pride picked me up. I put my head on her shoulder and gazed into our reflection without blinking. "Don't tell the others, but the magic show wouldn't be pulling in the crowds without you and me," she said. Her arms wrapped around me and supported my legs. She was right. "You're the real star. You're different from all of us. Magician is smooth, but his tricks are old and any promoter could find dancers to replace my sisters. You're really who the people come to see," she added. "Imagine what we could do together." Life was fun with Pride. She knew exactly what to say.

Pride made me feel warm all over, not the hot kind of warm, but the cozy blanket on a cold day kind of warm. We stopped as a group of pigs entered to fix a broken mirror, and I knew Pride would not be happy sharing the space. I leaned my head back on her chest, and she whispered softly in my ear, "The emptiness you feel inside can be filled with applause. Pursue fame with all your heart."

We made it out through the spiraling tube and found the others. It was almost time for the gates to open. I could hear the crowd at the main gate.

"Rabbit, it's time for your surprise," said Pride. "Our other sisters are setting up your party at the big wheel right now. Give us ten minutes. I hope you can solve the riddle."

The three girls ran ahead to meet the others. I could hardly wait. How was I going to kill ten minutes?

The noise from the entrance was getting louder. There was only one way in and one way out of the carnival. A wide gate at the front funneled customers through a snake-like gauntlet of souvenir booths. Calculated crowd control guaranteed a concentrated flow past every food seller and souvenir hawker. The psychology of the carnival fascinated me. The moving wall of sweaty people would be five deep soon. Every candy-faced kid would be screaming for a toy from the overstuffed and overpriced souvenir carts. Outside the gate, a line of people stretched onto the dirt field, all of them waiting to buy ride tickets. Tickets were sold only from one booth at the front. Families would overspend on tickets so they wouldn't have to walk back for more.

Not everyone entered the carnival. A crowd always stood around the fence. They moved and shifted with the crowd inside and tried to get a glimpse of a family member or friend. Unanswered calls and beckoning waves to leave the fun inside confused me. Why wouldn't they come in?

I studied everything about the hungry creature that was the carnival. The ticket trailer was the tollbooth. How much money was inside? The tickets bought would expire today, useless paper tomorrow. Greed and Gluttony hadn't used their fun house tickets, and I had the extras. I decided to find a family that needed a smile. Greed wasn't around to yell at me, so I headed in the direction of the line. I noticed the back door of the ticket booth was open. I had to get a look inside.

I shuffled out of the flow and planned my move. I'd hop up the three stairs, poke my head in, and check it out. Then I'd move around to the front and find a family to surprise with my tickets. I made it up the first two stairs in one hop, jumped again, and shot my head in sideways. I froze. Frog was sitting in a pot of boiling water, selling tickets and croaking in a voice emptier than any carny pig I'd seen today.

"Ow many tix yo wants? Das yo change. Ow many tix yo wants?..." The fire under the pot sounded like a thousand crazy people laughing. Why was Frog working the gate instead of the magic show? I recognized Frog from a tent show I had seen long ago. Frog turned. I ran.

Chapter Five – The Ferris Wheel

The Ferris Wheel. Was I too late?

I was close enough to see a pig at the platform. I yelled ahead. "How many cars on the wheel?"

"Ninety-one and a quarter," Pig said.

Ninety-one and a quarter? I looked up and guessed that he had given me the right number. I didn't see a quarter seat anywhere but quickly scanned the sides of the slow-moving boxes. Twenty-two, Twenty-four, I ran around the back of the wheel. Thirty-three, thirty-five, I made some quick calculations. The even seats were on the front and the odd ones to the back. The bench-style seating made four seats per car. I multiplied ninety-one by four. "Three-hundred and sixty-four seats?" I asked.

"Plus one," he said.

"One seat for every day of the year?" I asked. My face pressed against the fence that circled the bottom of the wheel and the mechanics that made it run.

"You're a genius," Pig said.

"YOUR birthday car." I mumbled. That's it. One car for every birthday.

I ran back around to the loading platform

while my brain wiped away old numbers and started a new equation. I panted out my request, fearing the party would start without me, "Could you bring down seat number sixty-three?" Pig didn't reply, but pulled the crank, mumbled to himself and yanked back on the handle. The boards at the loading spot sagged and the wood grain had been rubbed smooth. Years of Moms and Dads holding the hands of squirming youngsters had created a pocket on the platform like the seat of an old, worn-out chair. How many tickets had been torn on this ride alone?

"Sixty-three," Pig said and opened the car door. The hinges creaked with a crazy laughter.

"Happy Birthday," the sisters said together. Laziness finished behind the chorus by a beat. Envy and Greed grabbed my arms and lifted me through the open door. Pig slammed it shut. He then lifted a smooth wooden peg suspended on the end of a short rope and rammed it into the hasp, securing the eight of us. Smothered by the sisters, I couldn't tell where arms ended and legs began.

"We could split into two cars," I said.

Wrath poked her head into the middle of the car, "Nonsense, we'll tell you what to do."

"Leave him alone," said Lust. "It's Rabbit's birthday and the day is all about him."

"It's time for cake," Gluttony pushed to the middle with a cupcake and a candle. I couldn't see how we were all going to share.

"Is that for all of us?" I asked.

"Your cake, your candle, your wish," said Pride. "Have you thought about your wish?"

"I can't tell you my wish before I blow out my

candle or it won't come true." I said.

"That's where you're wrong," Greed said. "You don't know the power we have."

I was disoriented. The car moved faster, and the sisters blocked my vision of the carnival. I wanted to see the view from the top, but four of the girls stood on the corners of the car, grabbing on to the metal supports. One girl sat beside me and the other two across from me. "Do I have to tell you my wish?" I asked.

Greed spoke first, "If you tell us your wish, I can guarantee it will come true."

I couldn't tell if Greed was joking. I hadn't seen her eyes focused like that before.

"It works because you get something and we get something," Laziness said from her seat across from me. Pride leaned over from her spot above my left shoulder and added, "But the something you give us is something you don't need, and the something you get is something you've always wanted."

"What do I have to give up?" I asked. The motion had stopped, and I could tell from the position of the other cars that we were at the top. Fog swallowed up the car, and I couldn't make out the faces anymore. I waved my hand and Envy's face broke through the cloud.

"Your tail," she said.

"Just your tail," Wrath agreed, trying to control her volume.

I couldn't believe what I heard. The fog wrapped around my body, and I shifted in the seat so that I was turned onto my right side. Had Envy, pushed my leg or did the fog cause me to slip on the paint-weathered seat?

I looked down and I saw my tail move. One of my secrets was that I kept my tail wrapped up tight. Rabbits have round puffy tails, but somehow I had been born with a long skinny one. So I curled it into a ball with string. My eyes wouldn't focus in the shifting mist, but I know I saw the fog form a wispy hand that unraveled my tail.

"What have you always wanted more than anything?" Lust asked. I knew the answer but felt embarrassed saying it out loud.

"You can tell us Rabbit," Pride said, whispering into my ear. My mind raced. My wish had been the same dream I had always had, the same wish I made on every candle, every birthday.

"I want to be a famous magician," I said.

"We knew it," the sisters said together.

"Did you bring your lucky matches?" Gluttony asked. "I want to see you eat that cake!"

"Yes, the wish, then the cake. Just one bite seals the deal," Gluttony said. I half listened to the words. The thought of finally having my wish answered consumed me. I reached in my satchel and pulled out the matchbook. Of course, I would give up my tail. A rabbit has no need for a long tail. The sooner mine was gone the better off I would be. I'd be happy with glue and a cotton ball. Pride lit the candle and handed it to Envy who held the cupcake in front of my face. Wrath grabbed my right hand to transfer the cake to me. I could feel the matchbook drop back into my satchel as I leaned forward.

"Tell him how," Gluttony said.

Envy placed her hand on my knee and told me to repeat after her. "I Rabbit," She said

I repeated,"I Rabbit."

Envy continued, "Will give up my tail."

"Will give up my tail," I said.

"To have a great magic show," Envy finished.

Her wording was a little different, but I knew what she meant. "To have a great magic show," I said. I closed my eyes took in a deep breath and blew like I had one hundred candles in front of me.

"Now, eat the cake!" Gluttony looked to the others.

"Eat the cake," the sisters screamed. Something inside me felt strange. The closer my mouth got to the cake the harder it was to breathe. The fog choked me. They chanted over and over, "Eat the cake, eat the..."

"Stop," A familiar voice interrupted. The sisters scattered and the fog withdrew.

Seagull landed on the seat across from me, now empty. "Don't eat the cake," he said.

I looked up and Wrath hung to a steel beam about eight feet away, towards the center of the wheel. The other sisters were scattered above and below us.

Wrath's eyes were red, "Seagull, you weren't invited to this party."

"He has not eaten the cake, be gone." Seagull flapped his wings, and the sisters dismounted the giant wheel with the precision of seven terrified gymnasts. They ran into the darkness of the carnival.

"Grab the candle," Seagull said as my left hand shot up and pinched the smoking stick of wax between my fingers. Seagull hopped into the air with a quick flap of his wings and punted the cupcake over the edge of our car.

"What just happened? Why are you here? Why

were the seven sisters afraid of you? How are we going to get down?" I asked. I breathed deep but was even more confused. Everything had happened too fast. One minute I had my wish in my grasp. The next, I was stuck at the top of a massive Ferris wheel with no chance of rescue.

"Relax. We're safe for now, but we've got to hurry. They'll be back to feed you cake," Seagull said as he stood on the door and jumped. I looked over the edge and saw him stretch out his wings for soft landing on the loading platform. The wheel moved and I headed down. I placed the candle in my satchel and waited for the ride to stop.

"Get out," Seagull said after he pulled the wooden peg from the door and flicked up the hasp with his beak.

"You could have climbed down using your tail," he said. Another riddle or joke, I presumed?

Everything was still a blur. What had happened? I looked back at the wheel, and the only thing that popped into my head came out of my mouth, "Does this thing spin backwards?"

Seagull half smiled and said, "It does. Now follow me."

Entering a Special World

Chapter Six – Through the Back Gate

Seagull flew ahead and I was just short of a run. We had left the ride area and I weaved through tent stakes and ropes and kept an eye on my guide.

"Could we slow down?" I asked.

"Yeah, brilliant idea. Keep going." Seagull turned left at the last tent, the one where the giant carrot competition took place. The dirt path ended and we were back in the field. I saw we were headed for a part of the carnival I hadn't seen before. Darkness wrapped around me and Seagull vanished. I ran faster and he appeared out of the blackness ahead.

"We're here," Seagull landed on the top of a twelve-foot gate. More metal fence stretched from both sides of the hinges and disappeared into the carnival darkness.

"Amazing. A giant gate made in the shape of human hands," I said when my breath returned. I moved closer and leaned in to get a better look at the eight-foot sculptured hands. The palms of the hands were facing our direction. I tried to read the tiny engraved markings that covered every inch of the sculptured gate. "Is that writing?" I asked. Seagull stretched a wing in the direction of the left gate hinge, and I saw a magnifying glass hanging from a chain. The round metal that held the lens tapped the bars of the gate with the hollow tone of a single-note wind chime. I grabbed the handle and put the magnifying glass up to the gate. "Names," I said. Hundreds of names were carefully grooved into the palms of the large hands in just the small area under my eye. Each one held the flair of an artist's signature.

"Your name is there," Seagull said as he pushed open the right gate and motioned me through. I wanted to keep looking but dropped the magnifying glass. It swung back and I and moved through the gate. Darkness turned into light as we left the Carnival and crossed the threshold into somewhere new. The gate was tall but narrow, not at all like the wide main gate where Frog worked.

"Who knows about this place?" I asked.

"This is the Gate to Life. It's small, and few find it. This used to be the gate to the carnival before the Ferris wheel started spinning backwards."

"So, we found this gate. Where are we going?" I asked. "You've ripped me from my birthday party, scared away the sisters and stopped me from making my wish. I'm sitting right here until you explain." I sat down under a tree, no carrots anywhere. The light felt safe.

"I didn't rip you from anything good. You were about to make a deal that will rob your soul," Seagull said. "You wished your tail away and made a pact for something you'll regret."

"I won't regret being a famous magician," I was not going to let Seagull kill my dreams.

Seagull had landed on the grass beside me and pointed the tip of his wing at my nose. "That wasn't the wish. You said you wanted a great magic show."

"What's the difference?" I asked.

"If you had wished for a great show, you would have been trapped in that show forever. It's all about the illusion of words. You had a great show last night. Right? Well, you'd have a hundred more great shows before you realize you got your wish," Seagull explained.

"Magician?" Seagull continued. "Let me tell you about Magician. He knows the evil of the sisters. He met the sisters at the Ferris wheel on his birthday five years ago."

"You're lying," I said.

"Oh no, His birthday wish was that he would never see an empty seat at his show. He ate the cake and the deal was made."

"He's never had anything but sold-out shows for the last five years." I said. Was this true?

Seagull adjusted the newspaper on his head, pointed to the photo of Magician and said, "He got exactly what he asked for, but not what he expected."

"He's rich, he's famous," I said.

"It's the sisters' money. They fill the theater. Famous? At what price?" said Seagull.

"But he gave all that money this weekend to charity," I said.

"Charity? The sisters' favorite charity is themselves," Seagull said.

Everything I knew about Magician was an illusion. “What did he trade?” I asked.

“He traded his heart,” Seagull said. “The only reason he made the deal was to impress his true love. She had been to the theater once but never returned. It was a slow night and half the theater was empty. He was sure when he became famous and the theater was full, she would come back. On stage he has his sight but is blinded by spotlights and cannot see the audience. Off stage he is truly blind and cannot see an empty seat or if his true love returns. He thought he was giving his heart to the one he loved. It turned out he gave it up to seven sisters who stole his heart for evil. His eyes were the window to his heart.”

“Who left me the note to quit the show?” I asked.

“Magician,” Seagull responded.

“Why did he tell me to quit?” I asked. “He doesn’t like the finale?”

“He was trying to chase you away. The sisters were pulling you closer, and he knew your turn to ride the wheel would come soon,” said Seagull.

“He knew they were planning my party?” I asked.

“Yes. He knew your birthday was coming; the sisters would grab you and your wish would be twisted into something that would destroy you,” Seagull said.

“But I didn’t eat the cake,” I said. Seagull moved close. He wrapped his wing around my back and lifted my tail.

“You made the wish, and the sisters will stop at nothing to get you back to the Ferris wheel, force you to eat the cake, and collect their prize. We’ve got until midnight for you to change your wish and save your tail,” said Seagull.

“Why would they want my tail?” I asked. “Can’t I

make some silly wish to cancel out the bad one?"

"I'm afraid it doesn't work that way," Seagull said. "This wish must be the right wish. and you must return to the Ferris Wheel before midnight tonight to make that wish. When you figure out *your* right wish, you'll know why they want your tail."

I stood, leaned against the trunk of the tree and looked up. Tiny bottles hung by twine from every limb. Branches on one side of the tree were full of leaves and fruit—every kind of fruit. The other side was dry and withered. Bottles on the fruit side were clear and varied in color. Bottles on the other side were full of murky liquid and dead flies.

"What is this tree?" I asked.

"The Tree of Character," Seagull said. "Each one of the names on the gate match up to a bottle on the tree. One bottle is opened for each name at birth and sealed at death. The things you do in between determine how sweet the sound of your name is to others." He grabbed a bottle, untied the string, and held it up. It shimmered like gold. I put my nose to the glass, but Seagull motioned for me to listen. A mixture of honey and wildflowers scented my ear with a whisper.

"What about the bottles on the other side of the tree?" I asked.

Seagull tied the bottle back on the twine and stepped away from the tree. "You don't want to get that vile smell anywhere near your ear," he said.

Seagull raised his voice and started to scratch at something in the dirt with his foot. He tipped back the neck of a green bottle that had been buried. Pieces of grass poked out of the soft holes in the cork. Seagull pushed them away and grabbed with his beak. The cork popped out. He turned the bottle over, gave it a sidekick with his right foot. A piece of paper inside poked out of the opening and Seagull snatched it with his beak, all in one quick motion.

Seagull read, *"Birthday Lesson #1: Behavior. A good name is better than a fine perfume. Make the sound sweet to the ear."*

Seagull took off flying and I had no choice but to follow.

Monkey Meets Robot

Chapter Seven – Desert of Wasted Time

The field turned into desert. Sand started to swirl in a tight circle and blasted my fur, stung my eyes and crusted the sides of my mouth. The silhouette of a figure moved towards us. I heard the sand ping off his body and wondered if he were made of steel or aluminum. He moved closer, and I saw his right forearm was an hourglass full of sand. So was his left leg below the knee. His chest was a giant clock. His eyes were two horizontal slits that opened and closed depending on the blowing sand. A glass bubble on top of his head trapped a blue swirling cloud of smoke. His movements were precise, almost choreographed like a dance.

"Robot, this is my good friend." Seagull turned to me and wanted a response.

"I'm Rabbit," I said.

"A true, visual contradiction," Robot said.

"What?" I asked.

"What you say does not match what I see," Robot said.

Robot was the one not making any sense. "I'm a

rabbit; you're a robot and that's a seagull."

Seagull interrupted, "Forget it Robot. He'll figure it out. We'd like to hear your theory of time."

I wasn't following this conversation at all. "We would?"

Robot replied instantly. "Time sequences events, compares intervals, and quantifies motion of objects."

"Robot, don't give us the textbook version. What is the true meaning of time?" asked Seagull.

The blue smoke on top of Robots head swirled as he said, "Wind blows and comes back. The sun rises and falls. Round and round time goes. Streams flow to rivers and rivers to the sea. The sea is never full, and the rain returns to fill the streams. Round and round time goes." Robot continued. "Eyes can never be full of seeing or ears full of hearing. The things to come follow things already passed."

"Any questions, Rabbit?" Seagull asked.

"Those are all things I can't control," I said.

"Precisely," said Robot.

"If you can't control big time, what makes you think you can control small time?" Seagull asked. "Speaking in magician terms, trying to control small chunks of time is only an illusion. Have you ever tried to force water to boil?"

I never thought of time that way. Days turned into weeks and I couldn't make time stop. "Today's my birthday. I blinked and I was a year older. I don't want to sound depressing, but do you know how many birthdays I have left?"

Robot fiddled with a button on his chest, then started to sculpt the sand so fast he was covered in a cloud of dust. My lips wouldn't close tight enough to keep the crunchy taste out of my mouth. Seagull stood and watched. Robot finished, but it took a few seconds for the sand cloud to settle.

"Impressive." I said. He had crafted three identical blocks in the sand.

"Exactly one cubic yard for each of us. Sit," said Robot.

I climbed on the one to the right of Robot, and Seagull took the one to his left.

Robot beeped, whirred and spat out random stuff, "Some charge by the hour. Some pay by the hour. Don't waste another minute. I'll be with you in a second. Can we cram more into the time we have? It makes us equal. Everyone has twenty-four hours a day. No one can buy more. Pacing yourself? Some don't have enough time. Some have all the time in the world. Are there enough seconds to accomplish what is expected?"

Robot made sense in a nonsensical way. I felt the pressure of time every day. My list got longer, and my day got shorter. The faster the clock ran, the slower my dreams took shape.

"How many seconds do we have?" asked Seagull.

"Three billion is a long life," said Robot. "You're sitting on one billion."

I looked down at the block of sand. My eyes shifted to Robot. "How long would it take to go through all of this sand?" I asked. My long tail whipped around, and a few chunks broke away from my cube and fell to the desert below.

"One billion grains falling at a grain-per-second would take thirty-one years, 251 days, thirteen hours, thirty-four minutes, and fifty-three seconds," said Robot.

"You're sitting on a third of a lifetime. How will you spend time? You just wasted a year."

Robot pointed to the broken corner of my block. Was he talking about sand or the year I'd spent in the show with Magician?

"Some will never see two blocks of sand." Robot said. "Haste eats sand quickly. You can't be present pulling the future towards you. Yesterday won't equal tomorrow." Robot talked very fast and I tried to follow everything he said. I felt the pressure to accomplish my goals.

"How can I achieve a goal if I don't plan for the future?" I asked.

Seagull jumped into the conversation, "Don't live in the future and ignore today. Do what you need to do in the moment and tomorrow will take care of itself."

Robot pulled a neatly wrapped box out of the blue smoke bubble on top of his head. A silver bow circled the yellow box and was the work of a true perfectionist. It seemed he had measured each loop with surveying equipment. Why was he giving me a present?

"Open," said Robot.

I didn't want to be obvious about it, but I gently shook the box as I untied the bow to try to guess what was inside. I lifted the lid and was disappointed.

"An empty box?" I asked. As I turned the box over, I felt a tight and painful grip on my forearm. Robot forced the box upright.

"You have wasted enough," said Robot.

Why was Robot angry about giving me an empty box?

"You need to cherish what you have received,"

said Seagull. "You are in the Desert of Wasted Time. Each grain of sand that you see is a moment in time that someone will never get back, time squandered on bad choices and selfish pursuits. The grains blowing are time away from loved ones, time spent holding on to the past, and time spent agonizing over the future instead of living in the present." Seagull's voice pierced the wind, and I heard the words in a way that I hadn't heard before.

"Is there really something in the box?" I asked.

"A Moment of Truth." Robot said.

I looked again and I saw it. One simple grain of sand sat at the bottom of the box.

"A Moment of Truth?" I asked.

Seagull jumped into the conversation. "Those who pass through the narrow gate don't always know what to do with their sand. A Moment of Truth can show you that purpose. You'll know when it comes."

"The sisters say that carrot time is the best. Where does carrot time fit in?" I asked.

Robot moved his arm and pointed towards the horizon. "This desert is carrot time. It is fleeting, self-centered, unsatisfying and meaningless time. It blows faster than any other time, goes nowhere, and makes loved ones cry. You'll never find enough carrot time." Robot blinked his mechanical eyes as if to punctuate the last point.

Robot was right. The faster I chased time, the faster it blew away. Robot then handed me a small hourglass. He helped me place my tiny gift into the top section of the hourglass and sealed it shut. The light beamed off that one small speck as I dropped it in my bag.

Seagull buried his right foot in the sand and started

to move it from side to side. His webbed foot flicked grit everywhere. "Got it," he said. Seagull pulled another green bottle from the sand, popped the cork and kicked out the paper inside.

"Birthday Lesson #2: Appreciation. You are not in control of time, so appreciate every moment as perfect time. Sand is limited. Use it well." Seagull handed me the paper.

We left Robot and walked into the wind. I began to resent carrot time more with every grain that stung my face. I wiped crust from my lips, stashed the paper with the hourglass, and looked up. A door appeared.

"What's this?" I asked.

"A door," said Seagull.

Was that supposed to be witty? I reached the doorknob by standing on my toes.

"It's locked. Have you got the key?" I asked.

"It's not my door, it's yours," Seagull said.

"Well, I guess it's the wrong way," I said.

"Why?" Seagull asked.

"A locked door means the wrong way. We should try another route." I said

"Be careful. Closed doors may mean the wrong direction or a test to gauge how bad you want it opened," Seagull said. "Wrong assumptions on your part don't mean you get to use them as an excuse."

I looked to the left to see if there was another way around. Desert was everywhere.

"Is it time for you to open that door?" Seagull asked.

"I want to find the right way." I said.

The door opened.

Chapter Eight – Monkey's Last Hour

I walked through the door onto thick, fluffy grass. The cool blades reached up and tickled my belly. A gentle breeze met us and cooled my raw face as I walked into a bright sun. Seagull hovered over my left shoulder as we arrived at the edge of a deep gully. A bizarre, twisted tree stood lifeless beside us.

"How are we going to make it to the other side?" I asked.

"Are we going across?" Seagull replied.

"Why don't you pick me up and fly me over?" I asked.

"I'm a seagull, I've got no claws to pick you up or a beak strong enough to hold you."

"Well, I'm a rabbit and I can't jump across. I don't see any way to make it to the other side. Can we turn around and go another way?" I asked.

Seagull removed the newspaper hat from his head and opened to page two. "Tree falls," he said. Seagull then folded the paper and put it back on his head.

"That tree?" I felt the ground move and my feet slipped out from under me. Branches snapped, roots unearthed themselves, and I ducked to avoid being whipped across the back of my head by a limb. Seagull just hovered above me while the top of the tree slammed onto the opposite bank. "Did you make that happen? Your newspaper trick is scaring me."

"No. The tree was waiting for you to arrive before it fell," said Seagull. "Welcome to the Threshold of the Last Hour."

"The last hour of our trip?" I asked.

"Nope. Your last hour, as in the end." Seagull said. "Are you ready?"

"Ready to die?" I asked.

"Yes, are you ready to die?" Seagull asked.

"Not really," I snapped back. "This can't be happening."

"Nobody knows when it will come. If you fell into that pit right now, what would happen?" Seagull asked.

"I don't know. I hadn't really thought about it," I said.

"Most haven't," Seagull said. "It will come whether you are ready or not."

"So, am I going to die?" I asked again.

"I don't know; watch your step." Seagull said.

I wrapped my hands around two rotten roots in front of me and pulled myself around a clump of dirt. The earth under the dead tree crawled with white grubs and black beetles. Green moss hung from the top of the stump above my head. Birds chased more crawling bugs at the base of the toppled trunk. Rotten dirt steamed with a smell worse than the elephant trailer.

I climbed on top of the tree where it once touched the ground. Dead bark broke off under my feet. How would I cross without falling? Seagull was gone. Was this another test? Losing my tail and living with the sisters' curse was surely better than dying. I had the candle and matches in my satchel. Why couldn't I just make a new wish now? I didn't want to fall into that pit.

I inched out. Chunks of wood crumbled with each step. Tiny winged creatures crawled all over my feet and back under the covered trunk. I took another step and cold air blew across my body from below. Rope walkers look to the end, not down. I focused ahead. I couldn't see the other side but pretended I knew where it was. I took three steps without even realizing it. The sun was directly overhead and warmed the rotten wood. I could feel the shell around the slick trunk shift. Bugs had eaten the fibers that held the bark.

I stood over the center of the chasm. I didn't look down but sensed the heaviness of my unsatisfied life. Would my last hour be on this log? I couldn't talk to anyone, right any wrongs, or have any more fun?

I continued to walk the tree sideways. Ten more feet and I would have branches to hold onto. Cold air below hummed around the log. Then I heard a hiss. Was it air dancing in the crooked branches?

Something moist brushed across my left foot, but I refused to look down. Would a vine grow on a dead tree? The hiss sounded louder. I glanced down. Two eyes of a cobra stared back! I stopped cold.

The snake circled around my leg and then moved back to the bottom of the closest limb. Three and a half feet separated us, and I scanned my brain for what to do. Then I remembered the handler at the tent show. He

charmed snakes for a summer until one escaped and killed a pig who worked the carousel. I also knew that snakes ate rabbits. How could I escape? I had kicked off too much bark getting this far. Turning around was impossible.

I stared into the eyes of the cobra and knew I was trapped above the abyss. Both would swallow me whole. Death had never been this close. Could I wait? Night would come and the snake would crawl away, but I'd lose my chance to make a new wish. My options pointed to one chance.

I didn't need a flute; I knew it was showmanship. Snakes don't have ears. They are charmed by the swaying motion of the charmer. I moved ahead and pulled the paper from the pocket of my satchel. The note I found telling me to leave the show was the exact size of a playing card. I'd been practicing a routine to vanish a single card for months. The swaying motion of my arms might mimic the motion of a snake charmer. It was a choreographed dance of misdirection I had repeated a thousand times in the mirror backstage. His hood opened and he rippled back to the second branch. As he moved back, the snake grew ten times bigger. What now? What was the viper thinking? Was he planning when to strike? I swayed in rhythm with the song in my head. His huge neck and head bobbed in time with my motion. I made it to the first branch and braced my right foot against the knot where limb met tree.

I couldn't delay much longer. I risked breaking the spell. Don't reach too soon. Venom would kill me in minutes. I could break my branch and push him off. He'd strike. Forget it. I'd have one chance to grab and throw him into the pit. Music played louder in my head. Was I even strong enough? The card in my paw, my chest pounded. I felt a surge inside me. I vanished the card and lunged. My hand met the cobra's neck. I squeezed tight and felt the giant beast shrink back to his original size. I had him. His tail thrashed against the dead limbs and caught hold. I pulled hard. Bark slid beneath both feet. My weight shifted and I fell backwards. I held tight. My shoulder hit the trunk. I reached with my left hand, nothing. I slid off the tree.

I dangled with my legs wrapped around a branch; my right hand clenched around the snake's neck. My left clawed at the tree above. Six inches to stretch. His head twisted towards my wrist, hissing. Would the branch hold? I kicked my legs and started to swing. I felt bark with my left hand. One more time. Crack! We fell. The cobra's tail whizzed past. I let go.

I was safe, but the snake disappeared into the cavern below. How? As I looked back, I couldn't believe it. This ugly earthworm-looking tail of mine was wrapped around that trunk tighter than a python around its prey. I had forgotten about that pasta noodle dragging behind me. That tail had saved my life.

I climbed back onto the tree and headed into the branches. Retrieving the card from its secret hiding place, I placed it back into the outside pocket of my satchel. Hours of practice in the mirror had paid off big time. My mind raced and I thought about nothing but reaching the other side. My tail grabbed branches anytime my foot slipped. This thing had a mind of its own. Why had I kept my tail wrapped up for so long when I now realized I had another hand?

I felt more alive than I had felt in a while. Theater life had gotten so predictable. Life was show after show with the same script and the same tricks. I was on a wicked tree escaping death. I had a seriously helpful tail.

A small bird ahead of me was picking small sticks and straw stuck in the gaps of bark. His brown and white speckled feathers made him invisible against the background of the tree, but his beak flashed in the sun. I realized now that everything fit together. Each twig served a purpose. I wondered if the little bird was building a nest and what his family was like?

I thought about Robot and the desert of wasted time and reached down to make sure my hourglass was still there. This was certainly a perfect moment, a moment to stop and appreciate the never-ending circle of time. How did I fit into this world? A rabbit doesn't outsmart snakes and hang from a long tail. Did I have a purpose?

The bird was gone, but I noticed a small straw box sitting exactly where the bird had been pulling twigs. It looked like he had made the box as a present for me. Why was this bird giving me a gift? It was tied with a loose ribbon made from a soft reed. I untied the bow, lifted the lid and noticed a few small seeds at the bottom. I'd look at them later. I didn't want to drop them over the edge. I closed the lid, retied the ribbon and placed the box in my bag.

"Are you still alive?" Seagull asked.

"More than ever," I said. I ran around the last few branches, jumped onto grass and tackled Seagull. "Why did you put me through that?"

Seagull was flapping and pushing under me. "Get off, I can't breathe," he said.

"Sorry, I just feel so..." I couldn't find the right word. I had more questions for Seagull, but I wanted to tell him that I had listened to Robot. "Robot was right. I understand about the stuff I can't control; my time is a gift and life is full of snakes."

"Huh?" asked Seagull.

"Was that snake your idea?" I asked. "The charmer back at the carnival practiced his swaying motion to hypnotize the snake. I figured out that my card routine would do the same. All that practice paid off."

Seagull poked his beak into the grass, whipped it around in a circle, then grabbed the flap of turf, and peeled it back. Another green bottle appeared. Again, he pulled out the paper and read it to me.

"Birthday Lesson #3: Necessity. Pay attention to where excellence shows up in your life. If this activity were taken away, you wouldn't be you. It's a necessary part of you."

I took the paper from Seagull and squared it up with the others in my bag. "Where do we go from here?" I asked.

"Give me one of your seeds" Seagull said.

I handed Seagull the little straw box. How did he know about the gift? Could he see me on the tree? He opened the lid and shoved the box at me, hitting me in the chin.

"Pick one," he motioned with his other wing.

"How do I know which one to choose?" I asked.

"Look on the side." Seagull said

I reached in, pinched a seed, and turned it to the sun. Words were written on the seed. "This one says, Ready." I looked at the other two seeds. "Who wrote this?"

My gifts were the seeds of Ready, Willing, and Able.

"What'll it be?" Seagull asked.

"Willing." I said

"Plant it," Seagull said.

"Are we going to wait for this thing to grow?" I asked.

"Sure," said Seagull.

I bent over, scratched a little hole in the ground, dropped the seed and stood up. "Do we need water?"

"No. Look up." Seagull said.

The sky was incredible, full of big puffy clouds. I would lie on my back when I was young and watch the clouds bump into each other. Lions turned into giraffes and then got smaller and floated away. I didn't do that anymore. My birthday sky was a shade of blue I'd never seen before.

"There's a time to plant," said Seagull. "Today's a good day."

One burst of wind blew a tiny dark cloud above my head. I stepped back and watched a single drop of water land on the mound above my seed. Another breeze came and the cloud was gone. I looked down and the tiny seed had sprouted a leaf. Within ten seconds a stalk crawled out of the hole, and a collar of leaves opened onto the ground. The shaft rose five feet and bloomed a giant yellow head.

"Is that a dandelion?" I asked. Before Seagull could answer, the yellow bloom had transformed into a globe of seed pods with white parachutes on top. Seagull pulled the plant over in my direction.

"Pick one and hold on," Seagull said.

I grabbed the stick-part under the white fuzz. Seagull let go, and I was yanked off the ground. When the plant had returned to its original height, my momentum flung me into the air holding on to a seed-pod umbrella. My hand slid down the stick-part, stopped at the seed, and I was flying. Seagull took off and flew beside me.

Monkey Meets Boy

Chapter Nine – Sandcastles and Kings

"We'll land over there," Seagull said.

I wanted to keep flying. My dandelion glider was a better ride than the front seat of a coaster any day. Seagull was headed for a beach. The gold sand sparkled as the wind blew off the water. I saw piles of sand at the edge of the surf. Then my eye caught someone as he ran to meet us. The wind cut off on cue; I floated straight down and let go of the dandelion seed.

"Seagull, Seagull, Seagull," a little boy yelled as he ran straight for us. Then he turned for me. "Monkey, Monkey, Monkey." I looked at Seagull and sidestepped to avoid getting tackled, but I was too late.

"Uh, let me up," I said. "I'm a rabbit. You're a funny little fella calling me that." Boy started laughing. I'm not sure about this kid, but the diversion gave me a chance to brush off and pick up my shoulder bag. He was the classic little beach urchin. A mop of light brown hair flopped in the ocean breeze. He had dropped a green sand bucket and purple shovel on his dash to see us. His orange trunks had a yellow design that I couldn't make out because he wouldn't stand still.

"My paper?" asked Boy pointing at Seagull's newspaper hat.

"Later," Seagull said. "I want to see what you've been working on first."

Something shiny scratched my left foot as I stepped back to put some distance between me and Boy. I grabbed the shiny disc with my toes and bent my knee to bring it up into my left hand. It was a gold coin.

"Is this your coin?" I asked Boy.

"You take it." Boy said and ran back to his bucket and shovel. "Come see."

"We'll be right there," Seagull said. "Listen to Boy. He's wise beyond his years."

We followed Boy to the edge of the water. Six large sandcastles, taller than boy, stood in a row. These weren't your typical upside-down bucket castles. Unbelievable works of art glistened as boy carved a new window in the turret of the one closest to us.

"Bring my bucket," Boy said.

I was closest, so I grabbed the handle and couldn't lift it. At a glance, I thought it was sand. Gold coins filled the pail. Where did Boy get all this money? After I pulled the bucket to Boy, I looked back at the trench in the sand. There must have been more money in that thing than I made all year at the carnival.

Boy directed me to put the bucket in front of the closest of the six castles. "This king is rich but worries. He won't sleep or eat."

"King one was so stressed out about his money that he wouldn't sleep or spend it on food." Seagull interpreted.

Boy pointed to castle two and I lugged over the

gold. "This king had riches and lots of parties but sent no invitations."

Seagull continued his commentary. "King two had friends, tax collectors and salesmen spending his money for him."

I caught on, so I pushed the bucket to castle three. "This king had no son, and the jester got all his money when he died."

"King three died and because he had no family, his fortune was squandered by a fool," Seagull added.

Boy jumped around, laughed, and then pointed to castle four. "This king had buckets of money and a hundred children, but nobody loved him."

"King four had a large family and should have been happy, but the children wanted the fortune instead of their father," said Seagull.

The bucket got heavier with every push. We were now at castle five. Boy was speaking faster. "Everyone in this palace was greedy for gold and the villagers starved."

Seagull continued, "Castle five was full of dishonest gold chasers who were so self-centered they ignored the lesser people of the kingdom."

Before I could move the bucket, water and foam covered my feet. Seagull hustled around to the back of the castle. When the wave pulled back, twelve hermit crabs appeared. They scrambled up the mound of sand and knocked on a piece of driftwood Boy had used for a door. "Nobody home," the largest crab said.

This explanation about the kings and castles felt like a show that I had been invited to watch. "Are the crabs playing the part of hungry villagers?" I asked.

"We are hungry," said the smallest crab.

"Next castle," Boy said. I moved the bucket to castle number six and Boy continued, "And this King lost all of his gold and the prince had none."

Just then, a wave came in, washed away the last castle and the coins in the bucket all sprouted tiny wings and flew away.

"And misfortune carried away the money of king six," said Seagull.

"King six got robbed," I said.

"Expect the unexpected," Seagull said. "You can store up gold, think you are secure and bingo, it's gone."

Boy had started to rebuild the last castle while the crabs played in the sand. "Unlucky kings," I said.

"Not unlucky, they just loved money so much they robbed themselves," Seagull said. "Buckets of money can fool you into thinking life is secure but expect the unexpected. It will happen." Seagull said.

"Well, this is certainly a depressing birthday lesson," I said. "It doesn't matter what I do with my money anyway, I'm still going to fall off that dead tree one day."

"First, it's not your money. It's just a loan," Seagull said. "Don't hoard it or you'll be like one of the kings."

"You lost me," I said.

"Do you believe you have a purpose?" Seagull asked.

"Yes," I said. "I know that I'm here for some reason."

"Good. Your birthday is when it all started, right?" Seagull asked. "Consider your birthday a gift." Seagull started to walk towards Boy, who was coming our way. "With that gift came a happiness for something you can do."

"Like magic," I said.

"Yes. For you, entertaining is something that makes you happy. It's a gift, right?" Seagull asked. "The show makes people laugh, experience wonder, and you make money?"

"Sure. That was my wish," I said. "But you said I made a terrible wish."

"That's because you wanted fame for yourself in exchange for part of your birthday gift; your tail," said Seagull.

I looked beside my left foot and turned over a broken sand dollar with my tail. That tail had saved my life. Why did the sisters want to take it away from me?

"Are you listening?" asked Seagull. We had reached Boy and I bent over to get a closer look at sand dollar. Seagull continued, "Robot showed you how time is precious. Your talents and who you were born to be are precious. The money you earn from your talents is precious. Time, talent and money are your riches. Hoard them for yourself and you'll be like one of the kings."

"That's quite a math class," I said.

"Don't you think you should send a thank you card to the one who gave you riches?" Seagull asked.

"How do I do that?" I asked.

"You can't drop the card in the mail. You simply show how much you love your work, your family and your neighbor, with your time, talents, and money." Seagull said. "Once you've done that, the thank you card is delivered."

"That's it?" I asked. "I thought it would be more complicated."

"Reach down and grab a handful," said Seagull.

I scooped my right hand under the sand and watched the grains shimmer as they fell between my fingers and stuck to my fur. The little hermit crab scooted sideways to avoid being caught. This sand was different from desert sand. The grains glowed and sparkled.

Seagull pointed to the water, "Welcome to the Ocean of Gratitude. You are holding pure gold. Each grain is a thank you card washed ashore from the Ocean of Gratitude."

I started to understand. Seagull's riddles made more sense now. "I can help others and donate my time, sure. I can use my talents to earn money and would consider that a gift. But a wave could still wash it away?"

We stood so the water lapped against our ankles. Hermit Crab crawled around underwater and clamped onto the fur of my left foot when the water went out. She had started to warm up to me. The next wave brought a green bottle. Seagull picked it up and pointed the neck at Boy for him to pull. He dug his small fingers into the wet cork and yanked hard. Salty water splashed my entire left side as Boy back flopped into a small wave. Seagull took out the paper and turned the back against the wind.

"Birthday Lesson #4: Abundance. Be happy in your work and generous with your time and money. Create opportunities to use them for others."

I thought about the lesson and how I had tried to give the coins to Pig at the milk bottle game. Greed grabbed my hand and told me it was wrong. Greed wasn't around. Hermit Crab was at my feet again. I had a new friend. Boy showed Seagull new flags he was putting on top of each castle and I walked down the beach a few yards to think. Hermit Crab followed. She was the hungry one at the castle. I pulled the coin Boy had given out of my bag and handed it to her.

"For me?" She asked.

"You were hungry," I said. Hermit Crab grabbed the coin and headed for the water. I hoped she could use the money to buy some food. I didn't even know if a crab used money, but it felt like the right thing to do. The other eleven crabs greeted her and clicked claws together. A warm feeling spread across my chest. I started to walk and noticed she had run back and was pulling at the fur on my leg.

"Listen," she said. Hermit crab ran out of her shell, moved backwards into a spotted conch lying beside us and pointed to the opening she had just left. I picked up her shell and put it to my ear. A quiet sound started to roll from deep within the coils. A distant and soft echo sounded like the ocean.

"Thank you," said the shell.

Whose voice was it? It sounded familiar, like an old friend that I hadn't heard in many years. Why was the voice thanking me? I looked at Hermit Crab and one grain of gold sand stuck to her left claw, twinkled and fell to join the billions below.

Coulda Shoulda Woulda

Chapter Ten – In Search of Wisdom

Seagull and I headed down the beach. Hermit Crab was happy in my shoulder bag and I was glad to have a new friend. The sun was lower in the sky and I knew it would be dark soon. I thought about my wish and all the lessons I had learned. Hermit crab had neatly stacked each paper for me. The ocean was on our left, and dunes of gold sand were capped with sea oats that bent away from the onshore breeze. A lumpy dune grew higher in the distance.

"What is that?" I asked Seagull.

"You'll like this," he said.

The more we walked the bigger the lumpy dune grew. Other dunes behind this one looked the same. The low sun created long shadows on the sand, and the taller dunes darkened the smaller ones. A new musty smell greeted us.

"Books," I said. Piles and piles of books were stacked into mounds that stretched down the beach farther than I could see. Between piles, road signs of all shapes pointed up, down, and indicated winding paths. Seagull landed beside me and walked the last few feet that separated us from the first group. I loved books. A dusty brown one caught my interest and I picked it up to read the spine. Before I could get it to my face, I felt the pain of something hard hit the back of my head right behind my ear.

"Ow!" I rubbed the tender spot where a lump had already started to rise.

"Put that down!"

"What are you doing?"

"Get out of that pile," Three distinct voices bellowed from a pile of books to my right.

My knees buckled. There stood a plump little orange creature with three faces. It had scales and a lizard's tail but was plump and squatty. I thought it was cute and ugly at the same time. It had three mouths with wide gaps between crooked teeth. Four eyes were shared, and I had a hard time figuring out which eye belonged to what mouth. Short stubby legs made it waddle. Light colored spots and bumps covered its body. A tiny tuft of hair sprouted out of the top of its head.

"What are you going to learn from that book?" asked the trio of voices.

I dropped the book out of fear of what the creature might do. The bumpy knobs on its tail looked like they may hurt. I'd already been smacked in the head.

"I'm sorry. I love books," I stammered the quickest excuse I could come up with.

"They're full of knowledge," the mouth on the left uttered.

"But not wisdom," said the one in the middle.

"Studying too much makes you weary," finished

the one on the right.

"I shouldn't read books?" I asked.

Then they started in unison, "Look, knowledge can be found between the covers."

"True wisdom comes from the shell," the middle mouth said as the creature leaned forward, flipped the flap on my bag open and pulled out Hermit Crab. Crab waved her claw at me to say hello, pointed at her shell in agreement, and rolled off the creature's hand back into my bag.

True wisdom comes from Hermit Crab's shell? I had listened only once, but I couldn't see how a voice in a seashell was going to teach me more than books by smart people.

The creature moved in front of me and extended a stubby hand for me to shake. The one on the left spoke up again, "Maybe we need to introduce ourselves. I'm Coulda." He puffed out his chest proudly with arms crossed. "These are my sisters Shoulda and Woulda. We are the three faces of regret, and we manage the book dump. Most of these books are the self-help variety that tell you how to live your life. Got any to drop off?" Coulda leaned forward, looked around, and continued, "People usually feel brand new when they leave here–more alive than when they arrive."

"You said, regret. Those books are the cause?" I asked.

"Okay, girls, let's run down the list: bad decisions, shady investments, workaholic syndrome, not enough family time, and taking the wrong fork in the road." Shoulda pointed to a road sign behind her and continued the list, "Money, twisted prosperity, fortune telling, fame, tainted forgiveness, and pop psychology. The list goes on.

Look behind us. It's a gargantuan pile of wrong directions. It's the regret of following false wisdom." Each of them took inventory of their books. "You need to go to the shell to get the real story. Now, don't get me wrong. Books on how to juggle or do a card trick are just fine. That's knowledge, not wisdom."

I had to learn about my tail and what wish I could make. Maybe they could help. Totally confused I asked, "Are there any books about the seven sisters?"

Coulda, Shoulda, Woulda erupted into a chorus of laughter. The creature guided me to the right and pointed to a pile with frayed edges and bent corners. "We call them the carrot books. Go ahead pick one out!" The mildew on the top few books smelled ancient. Shoulda spoke up, "Here's a good one."

"How to ride life's roller coaster," the cover read.

"Have you ever been to the carnival?" Woulda asked.

"Many times. Some of my best memories are from the carnival," I said.

Woulda began, "There are thrill rides, junk food, games of chance, sideshows, fortune-tellers, cooking and eating contests, and rodeos. A carnival is the one place where you can indulge in everything all in one night."

Their shared tail started to swish. "That's how some people approach life. They indulge as if there's no tomorrow. They live with their hands up on the front seat of the roller coaster, cotton candy in one hand and a giant stuffed animal in the other. They blow through a mammoth roll of tickets and get in line to buy more. Year after year they keep going. After all, don't they deserve to be happy? Meanwhile the family, friends, and coworkers are standing outside the fence waiting for the carnival to end." Is that why a crowd gathered outside the gate and wouldn't enter the carnival?

I thumbed through the book as Shoulda talked. On page twenty-two, I saw a photo of a monkey riding the Ferris wheel. The caption read, 'Rabbit enjoys his birthday at the park.' The monkey was brown like me. Shoulda snatched the book, chucked it back on the pile, and continued. "Excessive self-indulgence leads to self-destruction if it's in pursuit of the wrong kind of happiness. That's why this pile of books is so high. Everyone loves reading books that tell them it's fine to chase carrots. Once they finally run out of tickets, the years of regret paralyzes them.

Life should sometimes be savored, taken in small licks like a strawberry ice cream cone. Life should sometimes be swallowed whole like the five-thousand-foot view from the basket of a hot air balloon—but not by yourself or at the expense of others. Happiness can own you or free you. There's *selfish* happiness and *selfless* happiness."

Coulda and Woulda had closed their shared eye and were letting Shoulda have the floor. "Carrot books are attractive because every opinion is a new way of living. You can take some from one book, more from another and decide what suits you best. You end up ignoring the wise voice that tells you which way to go."

Shoulda grabbed one of the signs off a nearby post, "Look at this sign." The road sign had the word "UP" printed in white letters against a red background. "You don't know if you should go up or down." As Shoulda turned the sign over, the word "DOWN" was clearly visible on the other side. You've got to know in your heart what you believe in. What are those things in the deepest part of you that light your path? How do you decide whether you should go "up" or "down"?

Shoulda started a ballet in the sand. As she turned the sign from up to down, She pulled off a spectacular cartwheel right there in front of me. "Well, you may think you're up, but you're really down." Shoulda held the sign with the word "up" facing out, but the sign showed the letters upside down.

I concentrated on the sign and thought about the carnival. The sisters made it fun, but something didn't feel right. I usually regretted all the carrots I ate.

Shoulda popped me in the head with the sign. "Ouwwee! What'd you do that for?" I asked.

"Are you listening? Have you learned anything?" Shoulda asked. "If you keep following false wisdom, you're going to be at the edge of your own cliff and there'll be nobody there to save you. The only thing you'll get out of chasing carrots are seven sisters that will steal your tail!"

"Oh." I couldn't move. The stuff that Shoulda talked about scared me. Were the sisters really my friends? Where was I looking for wisdom?

"Here, sit in this chair." Coulda pulled a rocking chair from the pile and whacked me with his tail, flinging me into the seat. "Now, close your eyes. Imagine yourself at the end of your life. You haven't got the energy to do anything but sit in your rocking chair and think about all the days gone by."

I shut my eyes and started to rock. "Slow down. You're supposed to be old and decrepit."

I slowed the pace and tried to concentrate on what Coulda had asked. I saw my fur turn gray. Then I hunched over in the chair. "Are you satisfied with how your life turned out? Could you have done anything different?" Coulda asked.

"Um, well, not everything. I mean, sure there are things I would've changed." I said.

"Change them now." Coulda smacked the back of the chair, launching me onto the sand face first. Harsh little creature—the three faces of regret. The grit in my mouth took me back to the Desert of Wasted Time. I remembered sitting on the block of sand with Robot. Coulda, Shoulda, Woulda continued sorting books. Seagull walked me over to a confusing display of traffic signs.

"Which sign is the right way? If you follow the wrong books, you'll end up on the wrong path," Seagull said. He took his foot and scratched a mark on the beach. "Today's your birthday. Do you want today to be your line in the sand that lets the world know that you aren't going back to the way things were? Use this new wisdom you've gained from all the pain of the past that you refuse to carry with you into the future. Is this something you want? Now, which way will you go?"

I lost track of the last thing that he said. My eyes locked on a small bottle half buried under the sand. I reached down and brushed the sand back from the front of the bottle. I felt like an archeologist uncovering a rare artifact.

"Time for another," Seagull said. He bit the cork, spit it out and pulled out the paper.

"Birthday Lesson #5: Name. Learn to discern knowledge from wisdom. Seek true wisdom. What is the name of the author of the wisdom you follow?" Seagull handed me the paper and I reached for the bag.

"Which way?" Seagull asked. I thought about the lesson, put the paper in my bag and cupped Hermit Crab in my hand. I lowered her beside the bottle on the sand. She popped out of her shell and found a temporary home in the bottle. Seagull laughed at the tiny crab, now with a giant home as I put the shell to my ear.

"The laughter of fools crackles under the pot," said the shell.

I looked to my right and saw a sign marked, "Swamp." I headed in that direction.

Chapter Eleven - When Monkey Met Magician

Carrots. How did it all begin? My mind wandered to the past as I headed for the swamp.

Before I started working for Magician, I followed the show from its early days in a traveling tent show. There was always a big illusion right before intermission. The curtain opened on a tropical island set. Seven beautiful women danced across the stage in lush green and ocean blue costumes that sparkled like ripples on moonlit sea. Each girl carried a torch that served as lighting for the scene. Magician helped Envy recline on a table then covered her with a purple cloth. Magician motioned with his arms, Envy floated eight feet into the air. The cloth was whisked away, and she vanished, only to reappear at the back of the theater beckoning the crowd to the lobby to buy magic kits, programs and candy.

I'd save money all year just to blow it on treasures at the carnival. Candy apples were dipped in a thick coating, tougher than a coconut shell. Popcorn was more burnt than buttery. I loved it. I made friends with the cotton candy lady. I'd pass by the gate on the way to school and buy a small bag. A coin's worth of spun sugar made me the hero of every kid on the playground. But the best stuff was sold after the floating trick.

I was hooked on magic. I had a drawer full of marked cards that never worked the way they were demonstrated. Two coins got me a silly mouse that was supposed to run up my arm and into my fist on command. I was too young to know the props the pitchman used were different from the ones they sold. Carnival workers had the script and the moves down to a science. This was their livelihood, and they were professionals.

Then a new pitch appeared. The seven sisters would carry the same torches on stage with a hand-painted backdrop of an island scene, always more faded than colorful, but it served the purpose. I knew the routine better than my homework. A sword swallower was first, followed by Magician, a juggler, then the dance routine, ending in the floating assistant. But the script for the cards and trick mice never came. Frog was introduced and something new was for sale.

Frog's pitch was classic, "Ow much is yo health worth Ladies and Gentlemen? It's priceless, yo know dat. Well, my friends, one shiny coin is all it takes to put a bottle like dis in yo hand. Das right, just a few of yo have heard about nature's true remedy, but all of yo will have da chance to take a bottle home wish yo. Dis little bottle is made from the concentrated carrot juice of five o da most powful remdies. Dis little bottle succeeds where all doctors, preachers and mudders fail. No harm meant to da mudders. Only dis can cover up what naws at ya deep down. It'll heal your money troubles, help yus get more dun, It'll show yo da shortcuts to take when you don't want to work as hard. It'll bring yo pleasure and chase away what fears yo."

Each bottle was labeled, and they had groups of bottles sorted by whatever the audience called out.

"Power," yelled a man to my left.

"Fortune," from somewhere behind me.

"Beauty," whispered a woman in the front.

I could see Magician standing at the back of the tent drinking from the same kind of bottle Frog was holding up to the crowd—a bottle labeled, "Fame." If some orange, mysterious juice could make me a magician like my idol, I wanted a bottle. I reached into my satchel, pulling out one of the coins I had saved all year. I needed this. This would make me a better magician faster than those worthless cards they sold last year. People started to pay. Most of the crowd stepped forward and shoved coins into the hands of the dancers and walked away with four and five bottles each. Magician took another hit at the back of the tent.

"Wees only brewed a measly batch. When da crate is empty, den dat's all wees got," added Frog. I pushed my way closer. "No bottles fo youngins."

What? They wouldn't sell to me? I just had to get one. By this time, I had made my way to the edge of the stage. If I pushed my hand between others, maybe they wouldn't realize whose hand was whose. My coin was ready. Then someone bumped me. I felt the coin fall from my hand and saw it roll through a crack in the stage floor. I had to find it. Where?

I reached behind the canvas that covered the support beams underneath. A bottle met my fingers. I leaned down and saw them. There were hundreds of cases hidden under the stage to supply the two-week run. Frog's speech was scripted to summon coins from pockets as fast as possible. He'd used the misdirection of scarcity. The spell of the pitch was gone, but I grabbed a bottle. I kept it hidden from view and grabbed another coin from my change bag as I stood up. It wouldn't be right not to pay for it. I placed the coin at the foot of the one of the sisters and slowly left the tent.

Monkey Finds Frog

Chapter 12 - Swamp of Desperation

"Swamp," I said wondering when the right path would appear and half expecting the swamp to answer. I was at the edge of a forest. The sky was darker, and it had started to rain. Seagull was not with me, but I felt Hermit Crab moving around in my bag. I couldn't find a path to follow, so I pushed through the brush in front of me. Moonlight filtered down and provided a dim view of the forest floor.

I didn't have a plan other than to keep going. The ground was cool and damp, and the smell of moss and bark crawled around the trees. Forest turned to swamp.

Knotty trees in front of me looked like the ruins of some ancient city. Something changed. The smell of rotting trees and stagnant water stuck to my fur made me gag. The moon was gone, but the flicker of another light, still deeper into the swamp appeared. The path was jagged and twisted and blackness was everywhere. Pools of mud beside me were thick and covered with clumpy green stuff. I concentrated on every step to avoid falling into the bog.

I approached a clearing and passed an old well with a broken wheel. A hand-painted sign read, "Swamp of Desperation." Two old grasshoppers with white beards dragged themselves across the path in front me. Maybe this is the wrong swamp, the wrong way.

"No," I hear from ahead. "No, yo are whar yo need to be," said Frog. The light I had seen was the fire beneath the pot. The laughing was louder.

"Did you make a deal with the sisters?" I asked. The stench choked my words.

"Since yo is almost one of us, I cans tell yo, yes," said Frog. His voice was deep and came from the depths of the putrid mud all around us and echoed against the hollow trees.

"Why are you sitting in a pot of boiling water?" I had to know.

"When yo chase dem carrots, yo don't notice how hot da water is gettin until it too late," said frog. "You traded yo tail; I traded my legs. Now I has to float in da boiling water of my choices."

"What was your wish," I asked.

"To be da one ever one come to see at da Carnival," said Frog.

Frog wanted to be the one that everyone came to see? He ended up at the ticket booth. He got his wish, but not what he expected. Magician's wish ended the same way. What would happen to me if I didn't make it back in time?

"Life fo me is jus a shadow," said Frog. "I gots no hope." Frog reached over the pot to cast a shadow on the side of a fat tree. A shadow-puppet rabbit wiggled his ears.

"Can I have it?" I asked. Without a word, the

shadow rabbit hopped off the tree and into my satchel. Hermit Crab shifted and moved to the other side of the bag. I had to get back to Seagull. I knew now that I didn't want to miss my chance for another wish.

"How do I get out of here?" I asked. Frog pointed to a break in the trees.

"It's da only way, cus of all yo done," Frog said. "Yo gotsa mighty beeg list o charges again yo." Frog pointed to a long piece of paper nailed to a tree. I squinted to see. My heart ached.

I ran to the opening and saw a pond, not full of water, but broken glass. I recognized the color and shape of the pieces. Could the glass be from a thousand shattered bottles of carrot juice–my carrot juice? The list on the tree was a list of all of these bottles. Frog said it was the only way out because of all I had done. Was my punishment a walk across the pond? Hermit crab squirmed. I knew I was supposed to listen to the shell, but this was my penalty and I had to walk alone.

I inched down the bank. The smell of the mud was thick. I closed my eyes and took a step. Searing pain shot through my foot and up my leg. Hermit Crab tried to jump out of the bag but I shoved him back. I didn't want to hear it. The next five steps tested everything I had. If I stood too long, my weight caused the glass to dig in. Shards stuck to the pads on my feet. If I wiped them off, I would cut my hand. I left them and moved on. I blocked the next part out and tried not to think about the blood leaving my foot and dripping down through the pieces below. How long would it take to reach the other side? I don't remember the last half of the walk. I kneeled on the mud at the end of my journey and grabbed a rotten leaf to wipe my feet.

The sting of my fur being pulled woke me from the daze of my pain. "Get up, Rabbit," said Wrath.

Chapter Thirteen – Seagull's Sacrifice

"Hi Rabbit. You left your birthday party too soon," said Pride.

"Yeah, and you forgot to eat your cake," said Gluttony. I couldn't speak. The sisters threw me in a small boat and pushed into a black ocean. This was not the Ocean of Gratitude.

"Where are we going?" I asked. My feet still hurt from the glass. Envy and Greed paddled.

"Back to the Ferris wheel," said Laziness who was almost asleep in the back. Dark waves splashed into the boat and icy water helped numb the pain in my feet. Hermit Crab was motionless. Should I have listened to the shell before walking across the pond? Would I be in the boat now if I had?

"Let him go," said Seagull. "He's with me now."

"That's funny," said Lust. "He looks like he's with us. Don't come down here."

"I'll bring him back before midnight," said Seagull. They were bargaining for me and I couldn't understand why. Seagull was the one I wanted to be with, but no land was in sight.

“No chance, Seagull. Fly away,” said Wrath. Then Greed stood up.

“If you fail to bring him back by the stroke of twelve, will you give us your wings?” The sisters repeated Greed’s offer. “Your wings, your wings.”

Before I could speak, I heard Seagull, ”I will give you my wings.” Seagull then pulled back, pointed his beak and headed for the boat. The sisters screamed and waved their arms to scare him away. Seagull hit my chest head on. My breath left my body as the force of the impact hurled me over the side of the boat. I caught a glimpse of Seagull as he pulled his wings in and curved away from the water. I went under.

Chapter Fourteen – Dark Water

It was pitch-black and the only light came from a full moon that was straight overhead. I sank fast and wondered how long I could hold my breath.

"Hello" a voice came from under the water. I couldn't see a thing. I kept sinking. "Hello, are you passing through?" My eyes had adjusted to the light, and I could see now that the voice came from a starfish.

"I'm fine. I fell out of a boat." I said, trying to exhale and not let water back in. "Where am I?"

"Where do you want to be?" asked Starfish.

I was running out of air, but I spoke in short bursts. "I'd like to be on land. I need to make a wish. I should have listened to the voice in the shell." I said. My bag was still with me. Hermit Crab had escaped and swam circles around my face as I talked with Starfish. My lungs burned.

"Do you need to breathe?" He asked. I nodded and a puffer fish appeared, locked lips with me, and filled my lungs with more air.

"Stay close," I said to Puffer.

"Tell me what happened," asked Starfish. I took another inhale from Puffer and did the best I could to explain without swallowing any water.

"I have these friends, or so I thought. We chased carrots together. They threw me a party and I made a wish. I promised my tail to get the wish. Now I need to make another wish so I don't lose my tail." Puffer provided more air, and I continued. "I thought I was a rabbit, but I've got a long tail." A big-toothed fish followed the wagging worm behind me in hopes of catching a tasty meal. I pulled it against me, and he swam away. "I'm not sure I'm a rabbit. I might be a monkey. A picture in a book looked like me. What should I do?"

"Sounds complicated," said Starfish.

Puffer gave me another lung full and I started again, "I've learned some lessons and want to make the perfect wish. My friend Seagull will lose his wings. I must be back to the Ferris wheel by midnight."

"It sounds like you may have come to a moment of truth." Starfish said. I reached into my shoulder bag and felt for the hourglass. It was gone.

"Is that what you're looking for?" asked Starfish. He pointed to Hermit Crab who was riding the glass tube and racing a pair of seahorses around a cluster of coral.

"You need a place to think," said Starfish.

I concentrated on Hermit Crab and knew I needed that hourglass. Starfish was still talking, and I shifted my focus. He made his way over to a giant shell and knocked three times. "You'll figure everything out in there." The jaws of a giant shell opened, and Starfish waved me in. The soft cushion inside looked comfortable. Hermit Crab swam in with me as the lid started to shut. How would I breathe? Puffer blasted an enormous air bubble inside just before it closed.

Chapter Fifteen – Moment of Truth

The shell was dark. I couldn't see a thing, but Hermit Crab had pushed the hourglass by my right hand. I gripped the glass and thought about what Seagull had told me in the desert. Those who pass through the narrow gate don't always know what to do with their sand. A Moment of Truth can show you that purpose. You'll know when it comes.

I broke the hourglass and felt the one tiny grain hit the back of my hand and tumble off. Everything had a purpose. The bird, the piece of straw, I understood. If a twig sticking out of a log had a purpose, I had one too. What was it?

That twig didn't have a birthday. I did. Everyone expects a birthday gift, but now I understood. The birthday is the gift. Everything about me is part of why I'm here. My fur, my hands and my tail are part of that gift.

I remembered each paper in the green bottles. ***Birthday Lesson #1: Behavior. A good name is better than a fine perfume. Make the sound sweet to the ear."***

Birthday Lesson #2: Appreciation. You are not in control of time, so appreciate every moment as perfect time. Sand is limited. Use it well."

Birthday Lesson #3: Necessity. Pay attention to where excellence shows up in your life. If this activity were taken away, you wouldn't be you. It's a necessary part of you.

Birthday Lesson #4: Abundance. Be happy in your work and generous with your time and money. Create opportunities to use them for others.

Birthday Lesson #5: Name. Learn to discern knowledge from wisdom. Seek true wisdom. What is the name of the author of the wisdom you follow?

The answer must be here in the lessons. Hermit Crab had fallen asleep and rolled against my leg.

"Wisdom comes from the shell. Only a moment of truth reveals what to do with your sand." I said. The noise was muffled, but the sound startled Hermit Crab.

"I'm in my moment of truth; give me your shell," I said. She crawled into my palm, released herself from the shell and jumped into the fluffiness of our underwater sofa. I held the shell to my ear and listened. Would the voice travel this far down under the water? Then a small whisper started at the very center of the coiled inside. The echo tickled my ear as the sound grew.

"Where were you born?" the voice asked.

Where was I born? Was that the moment of truth? The brightest memories were the theater, the fun with the sisters and my job with Magician. I had turned the light off to my past a long time ago. It seemed like every bottle had dulled my memory of the past. Foggy head. How far back could I see? I remembered the cotton candy in the school yard. Think harder. I had brothers. Where were Mom and Dad? When did I leave them?

Jungle. Why had I turned my back on the Jungle? A closed door in my head flung open, and a different kind of happy ran straight at me. I remembered. My friends and I would play coconut catch between the trees. Mom would make the best lunches, and Dad would take me and my brothers camping near the big waterfall. I couldn't believe I had let all of these memories get buried beneath my carrots.

Some of my favorite memories were when Granddad came. Now, it was all coming back to me. My grandfather had given me a special fork for my birthday. I sat on his knee in the highest tree in the jungle where he told me how he carved this fork just for me. He told me birthdays were special and I was born because someone loved me very much. I'm sure I was thinking about playing coconut catch with my friends, but I do remember what he said. "Monkey, when you grow up, you will come to many forks in the road. For some, the decisions will be hard and many will take the wrong path. As long as you remember Y.U.R.U. and listen to that voice in your ear, you will be going in the right direction." When he said the letters, Y.U.R.U., he pointed to each of the four prongs. "There's only one reason why you are you. Figure out that secret and your life will be a blessing to others." And look where I am now. The fork was like the road signs by the pile of books. Sitting on his knee, I listened as he told me about the voice. It all seemed so simple now. My life had been a series of poor decisions and wrong turns that had led me to the carnival, Magician and the sisters.

What did all of this mean? I had chased carrots, forgotten my past and had no good plan for the future. I was supposed to focus on the moment but had no idea how to start. What was I supposed to do? The seashell was still in my hand. I put it to my ear.

"In your Final Hour, sand will be sorted into two piles; desert sand and beach sand," said the voice.

I got it. I was born for a purpose. How I spent my time, money and talent was a reflection of how much I appreciated my birthday present. What I did every moment added grains to the desert or the beach. I had to focus on the beach. The one who gave me my birthday would count up my sand in the Final Hour and decide if I had accomplished my purpose.

The sisters, the carnival, and the carrots had turned me into a rabbit. I thought I wanted to be just like Magician. What he pursued was an illusion that tricked me. A childhood dream had turned into a terrible nightmare. The memory of my entire past suddenly poured through my body like scalding liquid from Frog's boiling pot. I had used my talents to serve myself. I wanted the applause for me, no one else. I hadn't done anything to serve anyone but myself. My talents had been wasted. I remembered the trees, the vines, and the wonderful time swinging with my friends. I had left everyone I loved to chase carrots. The sisters wanted my tail because it was part of my purpose. It all added up. I was born in a jungle and swung from tree to tree. Rabbits don't live in the jungle.

I AM a monkey. I had to find Seagull.

"How do I get out of this place?" I asked.

"Knock three times," said Hermit Crab who was crawling back into her shell. I knocked and the giant cocoon opened. Starfish had waited for me.

"I figured it out. How can I find Seagull?" I asked. Puffer swam by for another breath of air and Hermit Crab jumped into my bag.

"Puffer will get you to the top," Starfish said. "But don't forget this." Starfish pointed to the open shell. A gorgeous three-inch pearl sat where my grain of sand had been.

"Unbelievable, this must be worth a fortune," I shouted and tossed the pearl in next to Hermit Crab, the box of seeds, and the paper. I had forgotten that the matches and the candle and rabbit-shadow were in there also.

Puffer fish was breathing in and out as fast as he could. With one deep breath he puffed up five times his size. Starfish was holding him down and waved for me to grab a fin. I did and Starfish let go. What a ride! We shot to the surface like a balloon without a knot. Before we got to the top, Puffer rolled over and let go of my hand. I torpedoed out of the water and into a pile of seaweed on the beach.

Chapter Sixteen – Ready for Fruit

Seagull hugged me with his fluffy wings as I climbed out of the wet seaweed. My feet were better. A clump was wrapped around my leg, and I couldn't shake it off. With one quick snip, Seagull released me.

"Don't forget this," he said. Seagull handed me a green bottle that had been hiding under the mass of leaves.

"Let me get this one," I said.

"*Birthday Lesson #6: Accountability. In your final hour, sand will be sorted into two piles–desert sand and beach sand. How will you answer for where you spent your time, talents, and money?*"

"We've got one more place to go." Seagull said.

"Yes, I have to get back to the Ferris wheel," I said. "Which way?" I knew it was up to me. I found Hermit Crab curled up in the corner of my bag. She climbed out of her shell and found an empty pocket to call home. The shell felt natural against my ear, and I was getting used to hearing the voice.

"Which way?" I asked.

"Are you ready?" asked the voice.

I knew what to do. The ground was soft. I poked a tiny hole, reached in my bag and took out the box, and dropped the Ready seed. Seagull patted the dirt with his foot and waited. Just like before, a tiny cloud appeared. One drop of rain hit the top of the hole.

"My friend, are you ready to give up what you know for what you don't know?" Seagull asked.

"I am," I said.

No sooner than the words left my mouth, a sprout appeared. It had been barely three minutes.

"When you make a choice, you can be transformed. You can be in the same spot, the same fur, with the same troubles, but your beliefs change. You become someone new and the seed starts to grow," said Seagull

One little leaf quickly turned into four—four into twenty. The plant had turned into a vine. New leaves and vines were sprouting off in every direction.

"How big is this thing going to get?"

"As big as you want it to."

Seagull always put everything back on me. Where did I want to go? What are we doing next? He had a talent for leading by following me. It was magnificent. The seed had taken over the view of the beach and giant leafed vines started to block out the moon. The lush, green canopy that was growing reminded me of my home in the jungle.

"Are you ready?" Seagull asked.

By this time, the vines had taken off ahead of us and we started to walk into a garden of tropical blooms of every color sprouting from tiny buds that opened so fast the view above us looked like a fireworks show on a summer evening.

"This is incredible," I said.

The spectacle was so amazing, I didn't want to miss anything. The entire world smelled of promise. I could imagine myself relaxing all day on a leaf that had just sprouted in front of us. It was as big as an elephant's ear and looked softer than the velvet curtains back at the theater. A cool breeze blew across the path we followed. The vines grew ahead almost as if they knew our plan. If I turned left, so did the direction of the vines. The quiet whisper of rustling moss and the gentle explosion of curly green leaves played a song under our feet as we picked up our pace.

"I can't believe it," I said.

"Thanks to you," Seagull said. "This is your place, not mine. It came from who you are."

The giant leaves got smaller and the many vines turned into one. We followed the curling tour guide until it stopped at the foot of a tree.

"It's the Tree of Character," I said. "We've made it back to the gate."

"We've got to hurry," Seagull said.

I took out the shell. Hermit Crab went back to the pocket and I listened.

"Your fruit is how others will know you," said the voice.

I put back the shell and started to climb the tree. "Where's my fruit?" I asked. The tree was loaded with apples, pears, peaches, cherries, oranges, and more. Seagull sat under the tree looking up. "What if I pick a bad one? Is one better than another?"

"No bad fruit can come from a good tree," Seagull said. "Don't compare your fruit with others; each of us is responsible for our own."

I reached into the branches. What should I pick? The shell said my fruit came from the sound of my name. I closed my eyes and said, "Monkey." As the word left my mouth, I felt my tail move.

"You found it," Seagull said.

My tail had stretched over my left shoulder and picked a banana off a strong limb.

"Of course," I said. "A banana is my fruit." I had forgotten. "Can I eat it now?"

"Patience, you'll have time to enjoy what it can do for you later," Seagull said.

I climbed down, placed the fruit in my bag, and headed for the gate. "We don't have much time." Seagull was behind me.

"Slow down," he said. "You forgot this."

The patch of grass from earlier in the day was peeled back and Seagull was dumping the paper from the bottle.

"Birthday Lesson #7: Conclusion. Each of us produces our own fruit. Good fruit will serve others well," said Seagull.

We were at the back entrance to the Carnival again. I pushed open the gate, walked between the giant hands and headed for the Ferris Wheel.

Chapter Seventeen – A New Wish

Pigs gathered around the storage tent. Seagull flew above while I dodged the ropes tied to spikes angled into the dirt. A large pig stopped what he was doing and yelled to a group of younger ones unpacking a crate. "He's got the pearl," the pig said. How did he know? I patted my bag; it was still hidden. "The pearl," they repeated. A larger group of pigs had now gathered in front of us.

"Have you got it?" asked the pig in a group of four blocking my path. I saw the group behind me move closer.

"Don't let them see it," said Seagull. "They don't know how valuable it really is. They'll trample it and tear you to pieces."

I stepped to the left and threw back the flap on a red and white striped tent. A crowd had gathered to see the Miss Carrot pageant. Families were pushing to the front of the stage to get a glimpse of the contestants. I just missed bumping into a pole. A gap had opened behind the row of food vendors, and I needed to make my way back to the midway. I pulled back the canvas, looked, and ran to the next tent. The tent was empty. I ran through more tents until I was forced back into the main flow of customers by a shipping truck blocking my way. I heard something behind me and saw the shadow of three sisters on the side of the trailer. I'm sure it was Greed, Envy and Pride. I knew their shapes from the fire routine. I had watched their shadows on the back wall of the tent for years.

"Rabbit, Rabbit," Greed called out. "Rabbit."

Had they seen me? I couldn't tell where they were from the angle of the light. I backed up against a sign for dipped carrots and waited.

"Rabbit," Pride said.

I shuffled towards a food truck and stumbled into a bale of hay lining the walkway but regained my balance with my tail before falling. The front tire hid me from the shadows. Where were the sisters?

"There you are Rabbit," said Envy.

I ran under the truck. Three sets of legs circled. "You'll have to catch me," I said as I released the rabbit shadow from my bag. The sisters took off after the hopping decoy while I pushed out and headed for the neon. If this works I will have just enough time to make it to the Ferris wheel before they realized what had happened.

The fog hung low. The closer I got to the rides, the harder it was to see. Lines were long. Seagull wasn't around. The air was blacker than ever.

A young couple shared a cotton candy and pointed to the House of Mirth. "What time is it," I asked.

"Ten 'till," he said.

"Ten until what?" I asked.

"Midnight," he said.

Ten minutes and the carnival would close. My

birthday would be over. The sisters would find me. I had to make it in time. The wheel was loud and spun the riders into the thick fog as I approached. My mind played tricks in the mist. The cloud felt like it was growing thicker around me. I saw the pig from this morning still working the loading platform. My future depended on getting to that car.

"Bring down number sixty-three," I said.

"Can't do it," Pig said. "Everybody gets ninety seconds and this is the last ride of the night. Besides, that car is off limits, instructions by the owner."

I looked up and couldn't see the top half of the wheel. Cars descended from the fog, rounded the bottom, and disappeared on their way back up. I ducked under the gate and jumped into the spinning wheel.

"Stop," Pig said. "You can't do that."

My tail was the key. I swung from bar to bar and made it into the cloud. Light was dim, but I could see by the colored strobe of the lights on top shooting down through the fog. "Twenty-four, twenty-eight." I moved to the other side. Rusted metal and chipped paint fell like the bark on the fallen tree. "Fifty-eight, sixty." I let go with my tail and landed square on the floor of the car.

"Happy Birthday," Lust said.

"Hi Rabbit," said Wrath. "It's time to eat your cake."

Greed, Envy, and Pride appeared from the fog and climbed into the car, grabbed my arms and legs and threw me into the seat across from the others. Their hands were chains. I was trapped in their snare. Gluttony shoved the cake at my mouth. I turned my head. The riders in other cars looked and pointed as the Ferris wheel came to a stop to unload passengers.

"You must eat," said Gluttony.

Hermit Crab had moved from my bag and down my arm. As Gluttony continued to follow the twist of my head with her hand full of cupcake, Crab dug into my fur.

"Your wish must be finished," Wrath said.

"I want a new wish," I said. I leaned back but Wrath pushed the spikes on her boot into my back. The ride started to move again and Gluttony's hand hit my chin. Icing smeared across my cheek.

"Let go," Gluttony said. I had her arm with my tail and she couldn't pull away. Laziness gave a quick kick and my tail released. The wheel stopped.

"Hello girls," said Seagull. He hovered over the car. Hermit Crab ran to my wrist with the candle in his claw.

"Stop him," Wrath said, but the sisters couldn't move. The wheel started again. I knew I was running out of time.

Seagull flew down, grabbed Gluttony's wrist in his beak and held the cupcake in front of my mouth. Hermit Crab pointed at the cupcake. I moved him closer. He poked the candle into the center and clicked his shell with both claws. A spark jumped onto the wick and lit. This was my chance.

"You'll never be like Magician," said Envy.

"You could still be famous," said Pride.

Thoughts of the day flashed; the candle flickered. This was my line in the sand. I wouldn't go back.

I took a deep breath and started, "I Monkey, thank you for my tail and want to live for the reason you gave me my birthday." I blew out the candle as if there were a hundred. Seagull held tight to Gluttony's arm as I smashed my face into cake and swallowed without chewing. Large chunks, covered with icing, fell into my hand. The sister's grip on my arms loosened, but nothing had changed. "Are we too late?" I asked.

Seagull let go and said, "No, we made it. It's up to you to turn from the sisters and live your wish."

"Be gone Seagull," said Wrath.

Hermit Crab danced in my palm and pointed to my left hand. I moved her closer. She released her shell and backed into a leftover piece of cake. I knew the signal and raised the shell to my ear.

"The pearl," Shell said. I put my hands back together, Hermit Crab wiped off icing stuck to her back and slid into her shell. She settled into the corner of my bag as I pulled out my souvenir from the ocean.

"Get it," Lust said.

The bar on top of the car was a perfect swing point. I jumped, wrapped my tail around the steel and leaped into the fog. I flew for a few seconds. My hand caught a steel support and I pulled myself up. It was the single car. I hadn't seen it before because it was directly behind the lights at the top of the Ferris wheel. One last push of my arms and I would be able to safely land in the car, but tight chains wrapped around my leg. I looked back expecting to see a sister. It was the fog.

I switched hands, reached back with the pearl and waved it at the smoke. The grip released from my leg. I waved the pearl around myself and the air cleared. Why was the fog afraid of the pearl? I jumped into the car and more mist seeped under the door. I held the pearl at my knees and the smoke vanished again. The wheel had stopped, and I heard nothing from the sisters or Seagull.

The fog had now wrapped around the small car. If I jumped, the thickness of the mist would have caught me. From the back of the giant sign, the bulbs spelled, "earl of isdo." It was the only light in the carnival.

What was I supposed to do with the pearl? Did it have something to do with the Ferris Wheel?

I could see a control box off to my left. It was padlocked. I climbed onto the edge of the car to get a closer look. No cross bar was close enough for me to grab. Mist started to rise, then vapor gripped my wrist. Smoke pried open my hand and the pearl rolled off my hand and melted into the mist. I jumped. The fog didn't want me near that box.

Where was it? Thicker fog gave away the spot where the pearl had lodged between two bars at the center of the wheel. I broke through the cloud, landed on a cross bar, and saw a bubble of clear air forming a three-foot pocket around the pearl. Fog let me grab it, but I could not break back through.

"Need some help?" asked Seagull.

"Yes, can you move the fog?" I asked.

"Only for a moment, then it will be back," Seagull said. "When I flap, you go for the electrical box."

Seagull was right. He spread his wings and broke the wall of smoke. I could move through the mist, but Fog's hands clawed at my feet as I made my way back to the control box. The wind had picked up and Seagull was unable to fly without hitting the support bars.

I was back in the single car. I stood on one side and started to pump my legs up and down. My only chance was to rock the car, launch myself at the box, and keep Fog from grabbing me. I put the pearl in my bag so I wouldn't drop it. That box was important. I knew it. One more push with my legs and I was in the air. I hugged the box, repositioned and moved my head in front of a rusted padlock. I had no key. Dirt and grease disguised a label glued at the bottom of a shallow recessed shape in the metal. The slot was about an inch deep and curved like the box was smiling at me. I used the fur on my free arm to smear away the gunk. I felt the edges of the curved slot. I wiped harder. Beneath the layers was an old vinyl sticker of a banana.

"Rabbit," the sisters yelled from below. I could hear them climbing. Seagull flapped but couldn't make flight in the spiral of fog and wind. "Stop. Give us the pearl."

"Never," I said as I threw my hand into my bag. "Stay back." My left arm started to slip off the box. Fog thickened. I couldn't catch my breath. My hand came up with the banana and rammed it into the curved depression on the door. It fit. The padlock snapped open.

"Hurry," Seagull said. The sisters climbed faster and I fumbled for the lock. I pulled it off, dropped it and flung open the door. A round socket stared me in the face. Fog crawled up my back and grabbed my neck. I rammed my right hand into my bag and clenched my fist around the pearl. The cloud got tighter around my chest and my arm stopped. The pearl had to go in the socket. Seagull was grounded against the rail below. The wind blew faster, and the sisters were almost in reach of my legs.

Fog would not stop me. Small vines of vapor swirled in front of my face. Fog formed tiny figures of Magician, the sisters, and Frog. I saw myself in the mist. The grip hurt. "I won't go back," I said. The noise was muffled, and Fog filled my mouth. I couldn't breathe. My chest stopped moving.

I closed my eyes and concentrated on my new wish. I wanted to know why I was given a birthday. My arms were locked by ropes of mist. One of the sisters grabbed my foot. I felt my tail move. It took the pearl over my head and down into the socket.

A thousand angry screams shook the wheel and vibrated every ride below. The wind stopped and complete silence followed. No sound came from the box as I shut the door. Then the light came.

The sign glowed white. Darkness fled as light burned Fog down the wheel and out across the carnival. I saw the sisters scatter across the midway in different directions. Midnight glowed like the morning sun.

"You did it," Seagull said. Without giving me a chance to respond, he headed for the loading platform. "Let me bring you down."

I wrapped my tail around a long vertical bar and slid to the middle of the wheel, "Forget it, I'm climbing down this time." The wheel started to spin. "It's going the other way."

"You really did it," Seagull said. "You have no idea what you've done, do you?"

"Not really," I said as I dropped the last four feet into the bottom car, opened the door and jumped the final step. Seagull took me to the front gate. Frog was gone and the entire carnival was empty.

"Where are the sisters?" I asked.

"As long as you keep your back turned to them, they'll stay away," Seagull said.

"The field of carrots has dried up," I said.

"Should you plant something else here?" asked Seagull.

"Able," I said.

I reached in my bag and pulled out the box, "This is my last seed." I poked a hole in the ground, planted my seed and waited for the cloud. The instant the drop landed a tiny leaf pushed through. I put the box back in my bag and looked at the giant trees that now circled the entire carnival.

"Banana trees," I said.

"This is your carnival now," said Seagull. "Now let's go have a real birthday party."

We walked back through the gate and headed for the party. All of my new friends would be there. I looked up and noticed the lights above the Ferris wheel. Three new letters glowed and "earl of isdo" finally made sense. "Pearl of Wisdom," I said.

"Exactly," said Seagull.

The banana trees clapped their branches together. I took a bow and pulled Magician's card from my bag. I *was* born for something much bigger. I believe the Man of Miracles is perfect for *my* Carnival.

"Monkey, Monkey, Monkey" Boy ran towards me. Robot carried Starfish in a round bowl and Coulda, Shoulda, Woulda waddled behind them. I put Hermit Crab down to catch up with her friends.

"And Seagull, I couldn't have asked for a better

friend than you. I should have listened to you sooner. Thanks for your persistence. I'll admit your constant questions, riddles and prodding me to think was a little annoying at first. What really changed my thinking was how you told me about closed doors and open doors. When you told me they were excuses that helped me justify stopping. From that point on, I questioned everything I had learned and why I believed the stuff that everyone was telling me about my life and how I should live it."

"I won't forget the birthday lessons. They showed me I'm here to be amazing in some way. When I was chasing carrots, I was too stressed, too worried about tomorrow, and too distracted to be useful to anyone."

I grabbed Seagull with both arms and sunk my face into his neck feathers, "I've still got a lot to learn, but I feel like myself again."

Seagull freed his wings, took off his hat, and opened it to page one, "Monkey got what he asked for, but not what he expected."

Part Two

Birthday Lesson
Exercises for Discussion

Monkey's journey gave him new appreciation for who he was and for the gifts he was given. Work through the following questions individually or in a group.

Birthday Lesson #1: "Behavior. A good name is better than a fine perfume. Make the sound sweet to the ear."

What does it take to have a good name? When you think about character, personality and the effect you have on those around you, it comes down to what you do. We have heard the saying that actions speak louder than words and it is true. Deliver on a promise over and over, and your name will be as sweet as perfume.

You have three names, the name you were given at birth, the name you call yourself, and the name others call you which may not be your given name. These names can reveal your actions, personality or how you treat other people. From the perspective of others, are you known for being selfish or generous? Do you think you have the gift of creativity, but no one knows you by that description? Perhaps friends describe you as unreliable, but you see yourself as one who keeps a promise. I encourage you to open yourself up for constructive conversations with friends, family members, and professional colleagues. How would they describe you? Do you agree with what you hear? Do those names match the ones you have for yourself?

If not, you have some work to do to realign your name. Deal with any negative feedback one by one. We are not always our usual selves, but don't let repeated poor behavior define you. The only way to change your name is through consistent action.

Consistency comes from a set of intentional behaviors and by repeating positive behaviors, you can overcome a bad name. Yes, it will take some effort and some time. You may have to ask for forgiveness if certain relationships have become damaged. But if you are sincere and demonstrate a true desire to change, by consistent action, even the harshest names can be changed.

A word of caution: You cannot fake it. The desire to be perceived as honest with repeated behavior to the contrary will not fool anyone. True change must come from the heart.

This is not a business book, but we can learn something from a corporate approach. Companies have big meetings to craft their brand images and how they want their names to be perceived in the marketplace. They form a set of opinions about how they desire to do business which results in specific actions to support those beliefs. You can do the same for your life. Businesses understand their brand value is the most profit-producing asset they have. Trust in their names and the emotional connection customers have to the company translates into sales for their company instead of the competition. A product defect, bad review, or undesirable action by a company leader can decrease the brand value and cost the organization current and future business.

Your name is much the same. Its sound can illicit smiles or groans. What value do you place on your name? How will it, by association, help or hurt your family?

Understand and care about who you are and how you want to be remembered. Decide who you are in your heart and make a promise to stay true to that person. This is your personal brand.

Name three adjectives that you will live by and be known for:

1.

2.

3.

How will your actions support those "names"?

Birthday Lesson #2: "Appreciation. You are not in control of time, so appreciate every moment as perfect time. Sand is limited. Use it well."

Your golden time is your authentic time; time where you feel alive, productive, in tune with your talents. This can be time spent in work or play. If you are currently without golden time, you will need to be aggressive about adjusting your clock. Time is the great equalizer. We all have twenty four hours in a day. There are true health benefits to golden time. You laugh more, stress vanishes, and you live your best.

Have you ever been involved in something you love to do? Time flies; you do not realize how much chronological time has passed. Three hours has ticked away, and you felt as if it were fifteen minutes, a signal you have been in perfect time. You need to stop chasing the carrot that forces you to multitask and cram as many things into an hour as possible. Stop living for tomorrow and moving the future into the present.

What about the past? Do you find yourself dwelling on mistakes of yesterday? The past has served its purpose; let it go. Learn. Live now.

Chasing carrots and hanging out with the seven sisters will rob you of hours, days, months and years. Foolish pursuits and activities that harm your name should be examined ruthlessly. Draw a line in the sand to not waste your time on things that will squander your money, ruin relationships, destroy your health and tarnish your name. The desert of wasted time must be avoided.

Do you see how each Birthday Lesson builds on the previous one?

Name three ways that you can change your relationship with the clock:

1.

2.

3.

When do you lose track of time? Hint: You may have neglected these activities for years and you miss them. Name three activities you crave and desire the opportunity to get lost in more often:

1.

2.

3.

How are you wasting time? Name three things you must stop or start to change this behavior:

1.

2.

3.

Birthday Lesson #3: "Necessity. Pay attention to where excellence shows up in your life. If this activity were taken away, you wouldn't be you. It's a necessary part of you."

You have committed to investing in your name. You have adjusted your relationship with time and identified opportunities to involve yourself in activities where it feels like time stands still. Look back at lesson #2. Where are the areas of your life that have no relationship to time? Time vanishes when you are involved in this activity. Maybe you have ignored those pursuits for far too long.

What adjectives did you list in lesson #1? Did you always consider yourself a musical person, but you have not picked up an instrument for years? If you were to see a friend from many years ago, would he ask you if you still played? Was this part of your identity but you have buried it under distractions of work and life? Maybe your areas of excellence are hard to label. You love planning and organizing events, family activities, projects. Are you a numbers person? Do you use this skill in work and play?

Consider skills that have a specific label and interests that are harder to categorize. But, narrow your choices down to those where excellence and persistence are present. Your heart beats faster, you stick with it longer, and you think about the activity when you are not doing it. Others may accuse you of being obsessed.

I would like for you to list three activities or interests that if you woke up tomorrow and they were gone, you would not be the same person anymore.

1.

2.

3.

If you had to cross two off the list and keep only one, which of the three best captures the essence of who you are? Hint: The answer is often found in something that you have done since you were very young. Also, your list of three is often connected. If you cross off two, you will inherently need them to accomplish the one that is left. So, in reality, you will still get to do all three. Enjoy this exercise. You'll probably come back to this one multiple times.

What makes this one thing special to you? How can you use this gift for your family, your neighborhood, or for your city? Is this gift perfectly suited for something happening in the world today? Why is your gift not only necessary for your identity but necessary for those around you?

Birthday Lesson #4: "Abundance. Be happy in your work and generous with your time and money. Create opportunities to use them for others."

How we handle money has a direct impact on our lifestyles, our generosity, and our outlook on life. Has your pursuit of money created abundance or stress? Have you been slaving away for a paycheck that causes you to sacrifice your golden time in exchange for the status, security and toys that come with a hefty salary?

What would happen if the tide came in and washed your castle away, and your bucket of coins flew into the sky like tiny eagles?

When net worth is calculated, we often overlook the value of our time and talents that can be used to help others. The time you spend helping others and living your passion are times that can change the world.

Look back at lesson 3. You have one activity or interest that clearly defines who you are. Have you ever given this activity away for the benefit of someone else? If not, it is time to do so.

I am going to refer to this activity or interest as a gift that was given to you. You identified that if it were taken away, you would not be who you are. It is part of you, part of the person you were born to be. The way you show appreciation for this gift is to give it away to someone else.

I want you to activate your imagination and think of three ways you can give your gift away. Who is the recipient? When will you deliver the gift? (How? Who? When?)

1.

2.

3.

Birthday Lesson #5: "Name. Learn to discern knowledge from wisdom. Seek true wisdom. What is the name of the author of the wisdom you follow? "

The plethora of talk shows, self-help books and worldly advice on how to live your life is overwhelming. Everyone has a theory, idea, or formula on how to be your best, get the most, and die the richest. Are you a voracious reader? Has your approach to life been guided by one particular author? If you are not a big reader, has your vision of the world been influenced by friends, relatives, celebrities? Who do you seek for advice and guidance on important life issues? Do you believe in a higher power?

This is probably the most difficult and polarizing lesson of all. What one person believes is the right way, another person views as a foolish waste of time.

Coulda, Shoulda, Woulda are the embodiment of poor decisions from the past. You have your own experiences to help you avoid wrong turns in the future. You can learn from others and gain advice on how to navigate life from mentors, friends, and various leaders. However,

I caution you to be discerning in the ones from whom you seek deep wisdom.

As you sort through all of the authors of opinions, beliefs and recipes for the secret of life, keep asking these questions:

1. What is the original source of the message?
2. What kind of people does the message produce?
3. Why should you listen to the message?
4. Does anyone profit financially from the message?
5. What result does the message have in people's lives?
6. Where does the message ultimately lead you?

Birthday Lesson #6: "Accountability. In your final hour, sand will be sorted into two piles–desert sand and beach sand. How will you answer for where you spent your time, talents, and money?"

When most people are asked, they agree that they were born for a purpose. Have you ever considered who gave you that purpose? Do you believe that when you finish your time on earth, you will be asked to report back on your success or failure in fulfilling your purpose? How would you answer today? This lesson links back to lesson #5:

1. If you follow a particular author of wisdom, what is his belief on whether you will be asked to give an account for your time here?

2. Does that answer determine what happens to you in the hereafter?
3. Does your author of wisdom ascribe to a hereafter?

Birthday Lesson #7: "Conclusion. Each of us produces our own fruit. Good fruit will serve others well."

To find your "B.A.N.A.N.A.", you will need to work through each of the birthday lessons and identify how you will move towards being a person who possesses the right: **B**ehavior. **A**ppreciation. **N**ecessity. **A**bundance. **N**ame. **A**ccountability.

The combination of all of the Birthday Lessons, forms our Tree of Character. The condition of your heart is the source that feeds the branches that produce the fruit on your Tree of Character. You can go through the actions of each lesson, but if your heart is not true, the fruit produced by the branches will produce only bad fruit. A bad tree can never produce good fruit. The fruit that grows from the limbs of your tree will be different from the fruit that grows from the tree of your neighbor. We are only responsible for our own fruit. Will you be proud to display your basket of fruit?

Look back over Birthday Lesson #4. You named three ways you can give your gift away. This is your fruit. How do you believe the recipient will feel about the gift you have given? List the three people and what they received emotionally:

1.

2.

3.

I do not expect for you to complete all of the exercises in one sitting. Give yourself time to contemplate, discuss and work through your answers. Be willing to give help to others who are doing the same.

After you have finished look back and notice the connections and flow of the Birthday Lessons. (1) Working on your name is a commitment that helps you respect your limited time. (2) Now that you have adjusted your relationship to the clock, (3) you will have time to identify where excellence shows up in an activity. (4) This activity is something you will give away on a regular basis, for the benefit of someone else. (5) You now have a checklist to understand how to be discerning in where you seek wisdom. (6) Your level of success in these five lessons will determine how your sand is sorted and the quality of your fruit will be visible on your Tree of Character.(7)

If you enjoyed the book, Monkey's adventure, and the process of working through the exercises, you might consider a gift copy for someone's birthday. Also, consider leaving a review wherever you purchased the book.

The Story Behind the Story

Most of my career has been spent as a Creative Director in various ad agencies. One typical afternoon, I was looking for just the right illustration to include in a campaign. Stock photography and illustration catalogs were shipped to the office regularly, and I had grabbed the latest edition. The book fell open and a sketch of a monkey wearing rabbit ears metaphorically jumped off the page. I just sat there staring at this monkey. Why was he wearing rabbit ears? Did he think he was a rabbit? Why would he think he was a rabbit? The questions pelted my brain like a hailstorm in July. I tore out the page and pinned him to my wall.

Every time I looked at this monkey, I pictured him in a magic show. Magic has been my passion since I was four years old. It is the filter in which I view the world. I started performing shows for birthday parties to earn money in middle school. My high school years were spent performing over 50 shows a year for a Fortune 500 company. I later went on to produce illusion shows for a Paramount® theme park, helped organizations raise funds with sponsored shows and had a one-time gig in Las Vegas. I have operated my own magic theater in Myrtle Beach, SC and owned a magic-themed tour in Savannah, GA.

I have always liked monkeys. I wrote a letter to Jane Goodall when I was seven years old telling her I wanted a chimpanzee as a pet if she knew of any that needed a good home. In the nicest way possible, she wrote back to inform me a chimp would not be a wise choice for a domestic companion.

The story of this monkey in rabbit ears floated in and out of my head. Four years later, I had a book I was comfortable enough to distribute to friends and family for feedback. I then put the book aside where it sat for ten years.

I moved the cardboard box of drafts, illustrations and notes from Richmond, VA to Savannah, GA and ultimately to Charleston, SC. One evening last fall I pulled the box down, opened the manuscript and read it through in one sitting. As I finished the final page, I felt as though I had been reading a fable written just for me. Why? I realized I had lived the lessons.

The exercise of writing the book helped me sort through the wisdom, madness, and folly of my own life. Putting my own words down years ago, activated a desire in me to take Monkey's journey for myself. Looking back, I can see how wisdom written was not wisdom applied. Ten years were spent applying the Birthday Lessons to my own life. What you have just read represents about 80 percent of the original manuscript and another 20 percent that fills in the gaps, tightens up the story line, and provides a unique perspective from the other side.

You may enjoy looking at the inspiration references at the end of the book. As I read through the Bible and sought wisdom from the pages, the story of Monkey unfolded. We live in a broken world with temptation, bad decisions and an inborn disposition to selfishness. As I came to realize the stories in the Bible are no different than the condition of our world today, Monkey assumed a collective role many can identify with.

I believe that God is not only the creator of the universe and is still the orchestrator of all life but gives you freedom to move with Him or against Him. You were created in the image of God by his workmanship. You can see a glimpse of Him in your gifts and talents. His ultimate desire is that you would know Him, trust Him and embrace why He sent His son, Jesus, to die for our sins.

I can confidently say that if you earnestly seek to understand your gift, give it away, it will come back to you more precious than you imagined. You will live your life with a new purpose, a new direction, and with an intimate appreciation for who you are.

Your birthday was a gift given to you. You were born in a certain place, at a certain time, with a certain perspective on this world. You were meant to fit into a master plan and contribute your special something in your special way for some special reason. Enjoy this story, apply the lessons, and "Happy Birthday."

Jimi Gibson
Charleston, SC
March 4, 2020 (My Birthday)

Inspiration – Chapter by Chapter

Chapter One

John 8:44, New International Version
When he lies, he speaks his native language, for he is a liar and the father of lies.

Chapter Two

Isaiah 5:20, New King James Version
Woe to those who call evil good, and good evil; Who put darkness for light, and light for darkness; Who put bitter for sweet, and sweet for bitter!

Isaiah 24:23, New King James Version
Then the moon will be disgraced And the sun ashamed; For the LORD of hosts will reign On Mount Zion and in Jerusalem And before His elders, gloriously.

Chapter Three

Proverbs: 25:14, English Standard Version
Like clouds and wind without rain is a man who boasts of gifts he does not give.

Chapter Four

Proverbs 28:25, New International Version
The greedy stir up conflict, but those who trust in the LORD will prosper.

Ecclesiastes 7:4, New King James Version
The heart of the wise is in the house of mourning, But the heart of fools is in the house of mirth.

Ecclesiastes 7:6, New King James Version
For like the crackling of thorns under a pot, So is the laughter of the fool. This also is vanity.

Chapter Six

Isaiah 49:16, New Living Translation
See, I have written your name on the palms of my hands.

Matthew 7:13, New King James Version
Enter by the narrow gate; for wide is the gate and broad is the way that leads to destruction, and there are many who go in by it.

Ecclesiastes 10:1, New Living Translation
As dead flies cause even a bottle of perfume to stink, so a little foolishness spoils great wisdom and honor.

Ecclesiastes 7:1, New International Version
A good name is better than fine perfume, and the day of death better than the day of birth.

Proverbs 22:1, New International Version
A good name is more desirable than great riches; to be esteemed is better than silver or gold.

Chapter Seven

Ecclesiastes 1:6-7, New International Version
The wind blows to the south and turns to the north; round and round it goes, ever returning on its course. All streams flow into the sea, yet the sea is never full. To the place the streams come from, there they return again. All things are wearisome, more than one can say. The eye never has enough of seeing, nor the ear its fill of hearing.

Matthew 6:34, New International Version
Therefore do not worry about tomorrow, for tomorrow will worry about itself. Each day has enough trouble of its own.

Psalm 68:6, New Living Translation
God places the lonely in families; he sets the prisoners free and gives them joy. But he makes the rebellious live in a sun-scorched land.

Matthew 7:7, New International Version
Ask and it will be given to you; seek and you will find; knock and the door will be opened to you.

Chapter Eight

Ecclesiastes 10:11, New American Standard Bible
If the serpent bites before being charmed, there is no profit for the charmer.

Ecclesiastes 3:1-2, New International Version
To everything there is a season, and a time for every purpose under heaven: a time to be born and a time to die, a time to plant and a time to uproot,

Chapter Nine

Proverbs 23:5, New International Version
Cast but a glance at riches, and they are gone, for they will surely sprout wings and fly off to the sky like an eagle.

Proverbs 28:27, New International Version
Those who give to the poor will lack nothing, but those who close their eyes to them receive many curses.

Job 26:14, New King James Version
Indeed these are the mere edges of His ways, And how small a whisper we hear of Him! But the thunder of His power who can understand?"

Chapter Ten

Ecclesiastes 7:12, New International Version
For wisdom, like money, is a shelter, and the advantage of knowledge is that wisdom preserves the life of its owner.

Ecclesiastes 12:12, New International Version
Be warned, my son, of anything in addition to them. Of making many books there is no end, and much study wearies the body.

James 1:5, English Standard Version
If any of you lacks wisdom, let him ask God, who gives generously to all without reproach, and it will be given him.

Ecclesiastes 2:10-11, New International Version
I denied myself nothing my eyes desired; I refused my heart no pleasure. My heart took delight in all my labor, and this was the reward for all my toil. Yet when I surveyed all that my hands had done and what I had toiled to achieve, everything was meaningless, a chasing after the wind; nothing was gained under the sun.

Proverbs 2:12, New Living Translation
Wisdom will save you from evil people, from those whose words are twisted.

Ecclesiastes 7:19, New International Version
Wisdom makes one wise person more powerful than ten rulers in a city.

Ecclesiastes 7:5-6, New International Version
It is better to heed the rebuke of a wise person than to listen to the song of fools. Like the crackling of thorns under the pot, so is the laughter of fools.

Isaiah 30:21, New Living Translation
Your own ears will hear him. Right behind you a voice will say, "This is the way you should go," whether to the right or to the left.

Chapter Eleven

Proverbs 28:26, English Standard Version
Whoever trusts in his own mind is a fool, but he who walks in wisdom will be delivered.

Chapter Twelve

Ecclesiastes 12:5, New International Version
When people are afraid of heights and of dangers in the streets; when the almond tree blossoms and the grasshopper drags itself along and desire no longer is stirred. Then people go to their eternal home and mourners go about the streets.

Colossians 2:14, New Living Translation
He canceled the record of the charges against us and took it away by nailing it to the cross.

Chapter Thirteen

Proverbs 23:9, King James Bible
Speak not in the ears of a fool: for he will despise the wisdom of thy words.

Matthew 25:31, New International Version
When the Son of Man comes in his glory, and all the angels with him, he will sit on his glorious throne. All the nations will be gathered before him, and he will separate the people one from another as a shepherd separates the sheep from the goats.

Philippians 2:3-4, Berean Study Bible
Do nothing out of selfish ambition or empty pride, but in humility consider

others more important than yourselves. Each of you should look not only to your own interests, but also to the interests of others.

1Peter 4:10, New International Version
Each of you should use whatever gift you have received to serve others, as faithful stewards of God's grace in its various forms.

Chapter Sixteen

Romans 12:2, New International Version
Do not conform to the pattern of this world, but be transformed by the renewing of your mind. Then you will be able to test and approve what God's will is–his good, pleasing and perfect will.

Matthew 13:21-24, The Parable of the Sower Explained
But since he has no root, he remains for only a season. When trouble or persecution comes because of the word, he quickly falls away. The seed sown among the thorns is the one who hears the word, but the worries of this world and the deceitfulness of wealth choke the word, and it becomes unfruitful. But the seed sown on good soil is the one who hears the word and understands it. He indeed bears fruit and produces a crop—a hundredfold, sixtyfold, or thirtyfold.

Matthew 7:18, New International Version
A good tree cannot bear bad fruit, and a bad tree cannot bear good fruit.

James 3:17, New King James Version
But the wisdom that is from above is first pure, then peaceable, gentle, willing to yield, full of mercy and good fruits, without partiality and without hypocrisy.

Chapter Seventeen

Matthew 7:6, New International Version
Do not give dogs what is sacred; do not throw your pearls to pigs. If you do, they may trample them under their feet, and turn and tear you to pieces.

Isaiah 55:12, New International Version
You will go out in joy and be led forth in peace; the mountains and hills will burst into song before you, and all the trees of the field will clap their hands.

Ephesians 2:10, New International Version
For we are God's handiwork, created in Christ Jesus to do good works, which God prepared in advance for us to do.

2 Corinthians 4:4, New Living Translation
Satan, who is the god of this world, has blinded the minds of those who don't believe. They are unable to see the glorious light of the Good News. They don't understand this message about the glory of Christ, who is the exact likeness of God.

About the Author

Jimi Gibson has worked in creative advertising for more than 25 years. In addition to supervising the agency and serving as creative director, he has created brands that communicate what an organization is all about from a marketing and employer perspective.

His experience as a hypnotist and 30 years as a stage magician uniquely positions him to consult on a variety of techniques individuals and companies can use to increase revenue, engage in their community, and brand themselves for more focused results.

Search at TED.com for Jimi's TEDx talk, "You Have Magic Power: Use It For Good."

For information or to inquire about consulting and speaking opportunities, visit JimiGibson.com

To access additional resources, visit:
FindYourBanana.com

CPSIA information can be obtained
at www.ICGtesting.com
Printed in the USA
BVHW051110170821
614611BV00006B/775